Gold Stars®

Maths, English and Science

Big Workbook

AGES
9-11
Key Stage 2

PaRRagon

Bath · New York · Cologne · Melbourne · Delhi
Hong Kong · Shenzhen · Singapore · Amsterdam

Written by Paul Broadbent & Nina Filipek
Educational consultant: Martin Malcolm
Illustrated by Rob Davis/www.the-art-agency.co.uk
and Tom Connell/www.the-art-agency.co.uk

This edition published by Parragon Books Ltd in 2014

Parragon Books Ltd
Chartist House
15–17 Trim Street
Bath BA1 1HA, UK
www.parragon.com

ISBN 978-1-4723-6035-9

Printed in China

Parents' notes

The Gold Stars Key Stage 2 series

The Gold Stars Key Stage 2 series has been created to help your child revise and practise key skills and information learned in school. Each book is a complete companion to the Key Stage 2 curriculum and has been written by an expert team of teachers. The books will help to prepare your child for the SATs tests that they take in Year 6 and other tests that they take at school.

The books also support Scottish National Guidelines 5-14.

How to use the Key Stage 2 series

- Talk through the introductions to each topic and review the examples together.

- Encourage your child to tackle the fill-in activities independently.

- Keep work times short. Skip a page if it seems too difficult and return to it later.

- It doesn't matter if your child does some of the pages out of order.

- Your child does not need to answer the questions in complete sentences.

- Check the answers on pages 172-183. Encourage effort and reward achievement with praise.

- If your child finds any of the pages too difficult, don't worry. Children learn at different rates.

Contents

Maths

Contents

English

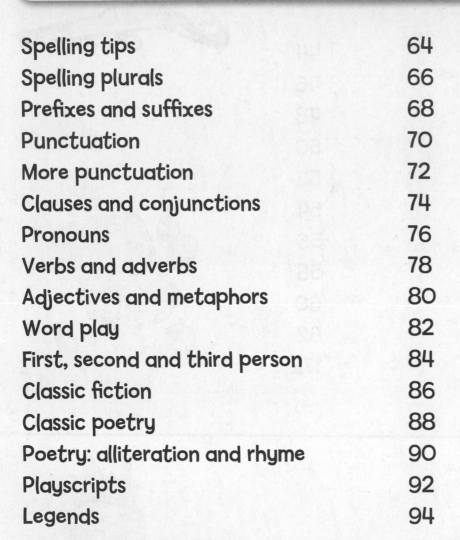

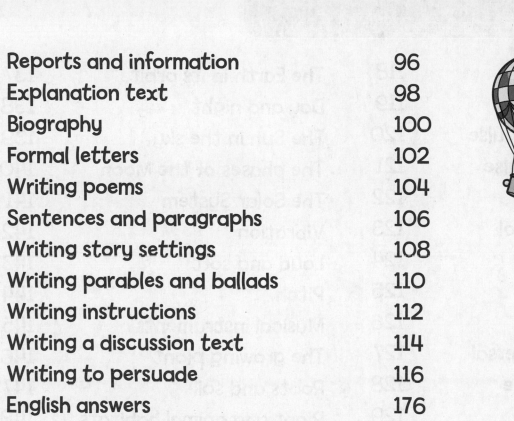

Contents

Science

Decimals

Learning objective: to read whole numbers and decimals

A decimal point separates whole numbers from decimal fractions - the parts of numbers that are less than 1.

Decimals are often used to show the price of things.

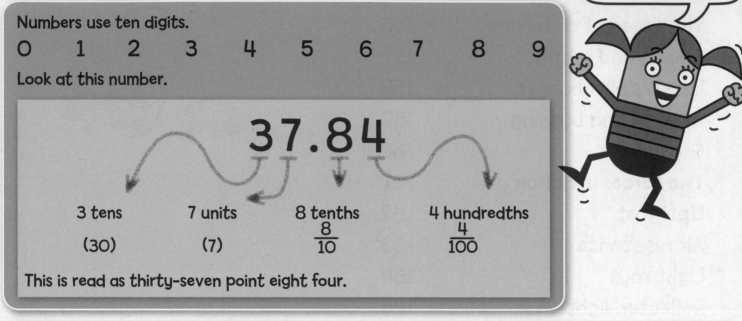

Numbers use ten digits.

0   1   2   3   4   5   6   7   8   9

Look at this number.

37.84

3 tens	7 units	8 tenths	4 hundredths
(30)	(7)	$\frac{8}{10}$	$\frac{4}{100}$

This is read as thirty-seven point eight four.

A Write the decimal number each arrow points to.

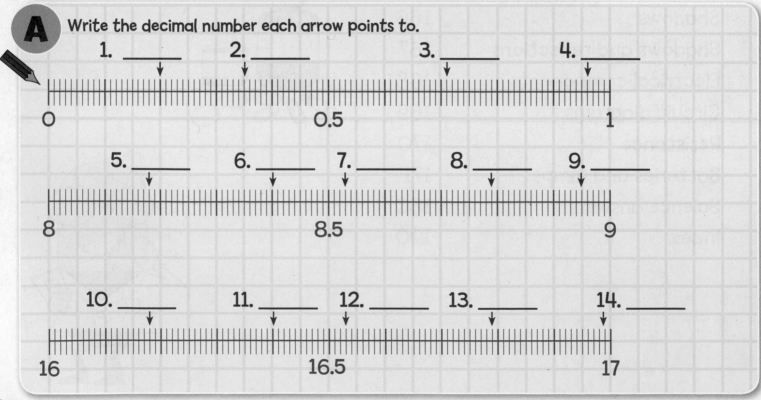

1. _____   2. _____   3. _____   4. _____

0   0.5   1

5. _____   6. _____   7. _____   8. _____   9. _____

8   8.5   9

10. _____   11. _____   12. _____   13. _____   14. _____

16   16.5   17

DEFINITION

decimal point: A point that separates whole numbers from decimal fractions.

B

This table shows the weight in kilograms of some of the turtles that swim in our seas. Write the list in order of weight, starting with the heaviest.

Turtle	Weight (kilograms)	Turtle	Weight (kilograms)
Flatback turtle	78.15		
Green sea turtle	355.3		
Hawksbill turtle	62.65		
Kemp's Ridley turtle	60.45		
Leatherback turtle	462.9		
Loggerhead turtle	257.8		

C

Rearrange this set of digits to make 6 different decimal numbers between 1 and 10. Use each digit only once in each decimal number.

1.

___.___ ___.___ ___.___ ___.___ ___.___ ___.___

2. Write the decimal numbers you have made in order, starting with the smallest.

___.___ ___.___ ___.___ ___.___ ___.___ ___.___

smallest →

11

Place value

Learning objective: to use place value to multiply and divide decimals by 10

The position of a digit in a number shows what the number is worth. This is what we mean by place value.

Making a number 10 times bigger or smaller is easy if you follow these rules.

To multiply any number by 10:
Move the digits one place to the left.

x10

| 3 | . | 6 | 4 |

| 3 | 6 | . | 4 | 0 |

To divide any number by 10:
Move the digits one place to the right.

÷10

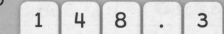

| 1 | 4 | 8 | . | 3 |

| 1 | 4 | . | 8 | 3 |

A   Answer these.

1. 1.35 x 10 = _____   2. 9.67 x 10 = _____

3. 68.5 ÷ 10 = _____   4. 334.6 ÷ 10 = _____

B   Read and answer these.

1.
A bucket holds 3.5 litres of water. How much water would there be in 10 buckets?

2.
A car travels a total of 9.85km each day. How far does the car travel after 10 days?

3.
A 250kg sack of grain is divided into 10 packs. How much does each pack of grain weigh?

_____   _____   _____

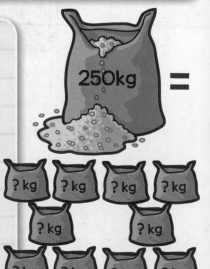

This is a super-square:

x10

7	70	700
0.7	7	70
0.07	0.7	7

÷10

Putting a zero on the end of a decimal number does not change the number. 3.8 is the same as 3.80!

C

Complete these super-squares.

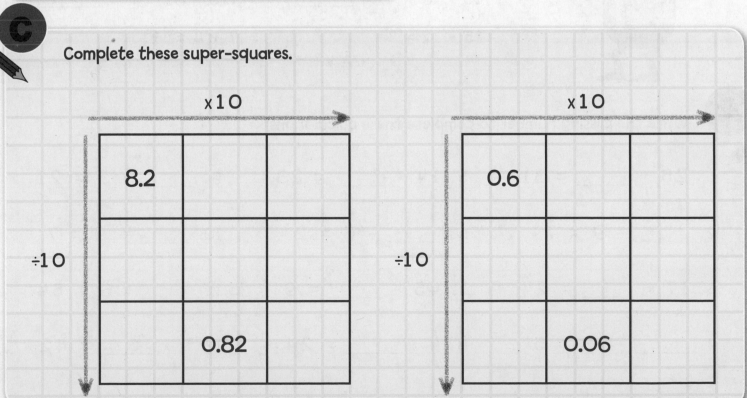

x10

8.2		
	0.82	

÷10

x10

0.6		
	0.06	

÷10

Mental calculation

Learning objective: to be able to calculate mentally and use brackets

Subtraction is the inverse or opposite of addition.
Division is the inverse or opposite of multiplication.
Use these facts to help you work out calculations with missing numbers.
Missing numbers can be represented by boxes, shapes or letters.

Knowing your multiplication tables and addition bonds is important.

$$\_\_\_\_ \div 5 = 8$$

Use multiplication:

$8 \times 5 = \_\_\_\_$ → $8 \times 5 = 40$ → So $40 \div 5 = 8$

When part of a problem is in brackets, you work out the bracket part first.

$15 - (8 + 4) = \_\_\_\_$ $(15 - 8) + 4 = \_\_\_\_$

$15 - 12 = 3$ $7 + 4 = 11$

A

Write the missing number to complete these calculations.

1. $25 + \_\_\_\_ = 31$

2. $\_\_\_\_ - 9 = 7$

3. $17 + \_\_\_\_ = 24$

4. $\_\_\_\_ - 13 = 5$

5. $14 + \_\_\_\_ = 23$

6. $\_\_\_\_ \div 6 = 2$

7. $45 \div \_\_\_\_ = 9$

8. $4 \times \_\_\_\_ = 24$

9. $\_\_\_\_ \times 3 = 21$

10. $\_\_\_\_ \div 9 = 7$

11. $\_\_\_\_ \times 6 = 54$

12. $7 \times \_\_\_\_ = 42$

B Write the answer for each of these. Remember to work out the brackets first.

1. (19 – 3) + 4 = ____

2. 14 – (7 + 2) = ____

3. (13 – 5) x 2 = ____

4. 16 – (8 – 3) = ____

5. 3 x (9 – 5) = ____

6. (4 + 6) ÷ 2 = ____

7. (8 + 2) – (3 + 5) = ____

8. (9 x 3) + (4 x 5) = ____

C Draw brackets to make each answer 12.

1. 19 – 12 – 5

2. 16 – 10 – 6

3. 22 – 5 + 5

4. 6 + 13 – 7

5. 24 – 6 – 6

6. 20 – 10 – 2

Try using opposite calculations to find the number.

D Write What's my number?
Work out the mystery number for each of these.

1. When I divide my number by 6 the answer is 8. ____

2. When I multiply my number by 6 the answer is 42. ____

3. When I double my number and then add 3 the answer is 19. ____

4. When I divide my number by 3 and then add 5 the answer is 12. ____

5. When I multiply my number by 5 and then subtract 6 the answer is 39. ____

6. When I divide my number by 4 and then subtract 2 the answer is 3. ____

Make up your own mystery number puzzles like this.

Learning objective: to know the squares of numbers up to 10 x 10

When two identical whole numbers are multiplied together they make a square number.

1 x 1 = 1
1 squared = 1
$1^2 = 1$

2 x 2 = 4
2 squared = 4
$2^2 = 4$

3 x 3 = 9
3 squared = 9
$3^2 = 9$

4 x 4 = 16
4 squared = 16
$4^2 = 16$

The numbers 1, 4, 9 and 16 are examples of square numbers.

A Write the missing numbers to complete this multiplication table.

	0	1	2	3	4	5	6	7	8	9	10
0	0	0		0	0			0	0		0
1			2			5	6	7		9	10
2	0		4	6	8				16	18	
3		3		9	12		18	21			
4	0								32		
5				15	20		30			45	
6											
7	0	7									
8		8		24		40		56		72	
9	0									81	
10		10			40				80		100

B

Colour the square for each of these in the multiplication table opposite.

1 x 1   2 x 2   3 x 3   4 x 4   5 x 5   6 x 6   7 x 7   8 x 8   9 x 9   10 x 10

What do you notice?

C

Circle the numbers in each set that are not square numbers.

1.   36   24   16   64   48

2.   25   81   9   15   12

3.   1   100   46   4   49

4.   18   49   9   81   77

5.   36   6   4   64   50

6.   49   9   39   100   92

Read across and down to multiply 2 numbers together. If you go across from 5 and down from 4 it meets at 20. So 5 x 4 = 20 and 4 x 5 = 20!

D

Answer these.

1. $4^2 =$ _____
2. $7^2 =$ _____
3. $6^2 =$ _____
4. $9^2 =$ _____
5. $1^2 =$ _____

6. $2^2 =$ _____
7. $10^2 =$ _____
8. $3^2 =$ _____
9. $8^2 =$ _____
10. $5^2 =$ _____

Multiples and factors

Learning objective: to identify pairs of factors and find common multiples

A multiple of a whole number is produced by multiplying that number by another whole number. Factors of a number can divide that number exactly.

Multiples of 3 →	3	6	9	12	15	18	21	24
Multiples of 4 →	4	8	12	16	20	24	28	32

12 is a multiple of both 3 and 4.
This means that 12 is a common multiple of 3 and 4.

Factors divide a number exactly.

10 has 4 factors because it can only be divided exactly by 4 numbers.

Factors of 10 in order: 1, 2, 5, 10
Factors of 10 in pairs: (1, 10) (2, 5)

$10 \div 1 = 10$
$10 \div 2 = 5$
$10 \div 5 = 2$
$10 \div 10 = 1$

Multiples mean more for me!

A Write all the pairs of factors for each of these numbers.

1. 8
    (__,__)   (__,__)

2. 20
    (__,__)   (__,__)

    (__,__)

3. 24
    (__,__)   (__,__)

    (__,__)   (__,__)

4. 28
    (__,__)   (__,__)

    (__,__)

B

Write the first 10 multiples for each of these numbers.

1. multiples of 4 ⟶ _____ _____ _____ _____ _____ _____ _____ _____ _____ _____
2. multiples of 3 ⟶ _____ _____ _____ _____ _____ _____ _____ _____ _____ _____
3. multiples of 6 ⟶ _____ _____ _____ _____ _____ _____ _____ _____ _____ _____
4. multiples of 5 ⟶ _____ _____ _____ _____ _____ _____ _____ _____ _____ _____
5. multiples of 10 ⟶ _____ _____ _____ _____ _____ _____ _____ _____ _____ _____
6. multiples of 8 ⟶ _____ _____ _____ _____ _____ _____ _____ _____ _____ _____

C

Look at your answers for Exercise B. Use the lists of multiples to help you find the common multiples for each of these pairs of numbers.

1. 3 and 5 ⟶ _____ _____   4. 6 and 8 ⟶ _____ _____
2. 4 and 3 ⟶ _____ _____   5. 10 and 6 ⟶ _____ _____
3. 4 and 5 ⟶ _____ _____   6. 6 and 4 ⟶ _____ _____ _____

D

Write these numbers in the correct part of the Venn diagram.

12   4   18
10   24   16
15   3   20
9   6   25
2   30   1

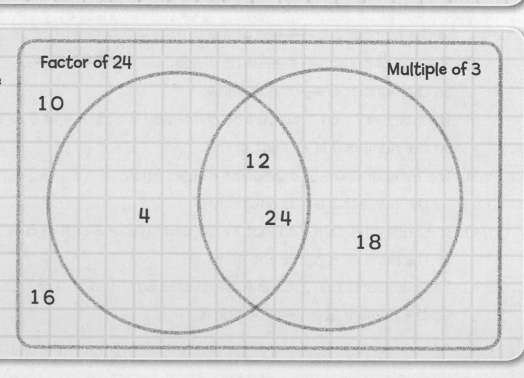

Factor of 24   Multiple of 3

10

12

4   24

18

16

Prime numbers

Learning objective: to recognize prime numbers

Prime numbers are special. You cannot divide them exactly by any other smaller number.

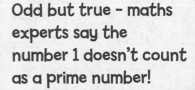

The only even prime number is 2. The other primes are all odd!

not prime

12 divides exactly by all these numbers . . .

$12 \div 2 = 6$
$12 \div 3 = 4$
$12 \div 4 = 3$
$12 \div 6 = 2$

prime

But 13 just won't divide exactly . . .

$13 \div 2 = 6$ remainder 1 $13 \div 8 = 1$ remainder 5
$13 \div 3 = 4$ remainder 1 $13 \div 9 = 1$ remainder 4
$13 \div 4 = 3$ remainder 1 $13 \div 10 = 1$ remainder 3
$13 \div 5 = 2$ remainder 3 $13 \div 11 = 1$ remainder 2
$13 \div 6 = 2$ remainder 1 $13 \div 12 = 1$ remainder 1
$13 \div 7 = 1$ remainder 6

A

Cross out the words to show the primes. The first two have been done for you.

1. The number 5 ~~can~~ / cannot be divided by 2 or 3 or 4.
   So the number 5 is / ~~is not~~ prime.

2. The number 6 can / ~~cannot~~ be divided by 2 or 3 ~~or 4 or 5~~.
   So the number 6 ~~is~~ / is not prime.

3. The number 7 can / cannot be divided by 2 or 3 or 4 or 5 or 6.
   So the number 7 is / is not prime.

4. The number 3 can / cannot be divided by 2.
   So the number 3 is / is not prime.

5. The number 8 can / cannot be divided by 2 or 3 or 4 or 5 or 6 or 7.
   So the number 8 is / is not prime.

6. The number 11 can / cannot be divided by 2 or 3 or 4 or 5 or 6 or 7 or 8 or 9 or 10.
   So the number 11 is / is not prime.

Odd but true – maths experts say the number 1 doesn't count as a prime number!

B

All the numbers in the green box can be divided by 2, 3 or 5 . . .
except for the prime numbers. Circle six more hidden primes.

15		48		25		(7)		18		44
	62		11		20		12		36	
50		14		6		22		13		75
	30		17		16		10		4	
90		26		24		27		33		19
	100		35		55		60		8	
70		9		23		16		21		22
	29		86		64		85		40	

C

This poem helps you remember all the prime numbers up to 20.
Fill in the missing rhymes.

| **missing rhymes** |
| seventeen   two |
| eleven   nineteen |
| five   thirteen |

They can't be divided, whatever you do

The smallest prime is number _____

Then come three and _____ and seven

The next prime is of course _____

_____ is next upon the scene

_____ follows and then _____.

Written addition

Learning objective: to use efficient written methods to add whole numbers

When you add numbers like this, it helps to line up the columns. If a column adds up to 10 or more, carry the 10 over to the next column by writing a small number 1 beneath. Then add it with the numbers in that column.

The columns are: thousands, hundreds, tens and units.

What is 3492 added to 2631?

```
   Th H T U
      3 4 9 2
   +  2 6 3 1
   ----------
      6 1 2 3
        1 1
```

Look out for addition words in problems: add, total, sum, altogether, greater than...

A Answer these.

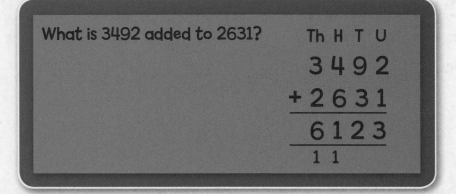

```
1.   6 7 2 8        2.   3 1 2 8        3.   1 5 6 1
   + 2 7 4 0           + 4 6 7 5           + 2 9 1 8
```

B Read and answer these. Use a pen and paper to work out each calculation.

1. Add together 3945 and 5680. _____

2. What is 5929 and 3874 added together? _____

3. What is the sum of 2263 and 3815? _____

4. Total 5923 and 1946. _____

5. What is the total of 4328 and 2749? _____

6. What number is 4444 greater than 1991? _____

22

DEFINITION

addition: Finding the total of two or more numbers. The + sign shows that numbers are being added together.

C

Look at these distances and work out the different totals.

A → 1652km   B → 3559km   C → 3081km   D → 2722 km   E → 1768km

1. A + E   →   _____ km

2. D + C   →   _____ km

3. B + D   →   _____ km

4. C + E   →   _____ km

5. E + D   →   _____ km

D

All the digits 1 and 3 are missing.

Write the digits 1 or 3 in the correct place to complete this addition.

```
    4 6 [ ] 8
  +
      9 [ ] 6 [ ]
  _____
  [ ][ ] 8 0 [ ]
```

Use your knowledge of place value.

Write the numbers 1 and 3 on six small pieces of paper and try them in the different missing boxes to see which ones work.

Written subtraction

Learning objective: to use efficient written methods to subtract whole numbers

There are different ways of taking one number away from another.
If you can't work it out in your head you can try a written method.

Example
What is 3674 subtract 1738?

Step 1

Think of 70 + 4 as 60 + 14

14 - 8 = 6

$$3\ 6\ {}^6\!\!\!\not7\ {}^1\!4$$
$$-1\ 7\ 3\ 8$$
$$6$$

Step 2

60 - 30 = 30

$$3\ 6\ {}^6\!\!\!\not7\ {}^1\!4$$
$$-1\ 7\ 3\ 8$$
$$3\ 6$$

Make sure you line up the columns correctly.

Step 3

Think of 3000 + 600 as 2000 + 1600.

1600 - 700 = 900

$${}^2\!\!\!\not3\ {}^1\!6\ {}^6\!\!\!\not7\ {}^1\!4$$
$$-1\ 7\ 3\ 8$$
$$9\ 3\ 6$$

Step 4

2000 - 1000 = 1000

$${}^2\!\!\!\not3\ {}^1\!6\ {}^6\!\!\!\not7\ {}^1\!4$$
$$-1\ 7\ 3\ 8$$
$$1\ 9\ 3\ 6$$

A Write the answers.

1.
$$4\ 7\ 3\ 8$$
$$-1\ 5\ 9\ 2$$

2.
$$9\ 4\ 7\ 1$$
$$-3\ 8\ 0\ 3$$

3.
$$6\ 5\ 4\ 5$$
$$-2\ 1\ 7\ 5$$

DEFINITION

subtraction: Taking one number away from another. The - sign shows one number is being taken away from another.

B

Write the missing digits in these subtractions.

1.
```
    3 8 4 □
  - 1 7 □ 2
  ─────────
    2 □ 8 5
```

2.
```
    7 □ 4 3
  - 2 4 8 □
  ─────────
    □ 4 5 7
```

3.
```
    4 1 1 5
  - 2 □ 3 □
  ─────────
    □ 1 7 9
```

C

This table shows the depths of the deepest oceans and seas in the world.

Look at the table and answer the questions.

Ocean/sea	Average depth (metres)
Pacific Ocean	4028 m
Indian Ocean	3963 m
Atlantic Ocean	3926 m
Caribbean Sea	2647 m
South China Sea	1652 m
Bering Sea	1547 m
Gulf of Mexico	1486 m
Mediterranean Sea	1429 m

1. How much deeper is the Caribbean Sea than the Gulf of Mexico?

2. By how many metres is the Pacific Ocean deeper than the Caribbean Sea?

3. What is the difference in depth between the Atlantic Ocean and the Caribbean Sea?

4. Which two seas have a difference in depth of 1100m?

5. Which sea is 1316m less in depth than the Indian Ocean?

6. Which two oceans or seas have the smallest difference in depth?

Written multiplication

Learning objective: to use written methods to multiply
TU (tens and units) x TU

When you need to multiply two numbers together, decide whether you are able to work out the answer in your head, or whether you need to use a written method.

Look at these two written methods for 34 x 26.

Method 1

x	30	4		
20	600	80	→	680
6	180	24	→	+ 204
				884

Method 2

```
    3 4
  x 2 6
  ─────
  2 0 4     (3 4 x 6)
  6 8 0     (3 4 x 2 0)
  ─────
  8 8 4
```

It is always a good idea to estimate the answer first and then check your final answer with your estimate.

A   Complete these multiplications.

1. 1 9 x 7 6 = _____

2. 8 4 x 3 7 = _____

3.   1 9
      x 2 4

4.   5 3
      x 6 2

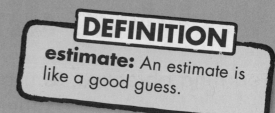

DEFINITION

estimate: An estimate is like a good guess.

B   Read and answer these questions.

1. There are 24 hours in a day. How many hours are there in September? _____

2. A truck makes a 58km journey 16 times in a week. How far does the truck travel in total? _____

3. A packet of nuts weighs 28g and there are 25 packets in a box. How many grams of nuts are there in a full box? _____

4. There are 15 pencils in a pack and a school orders 49 packs. How many pencils will there be altogether? _____

C

How many of each item has been ordered?

This is an order form for equipment for a school.

Items	Amount in 1 pack	Number of packs	Total number of items
Pencils	28	76	
Chalk	15	33	
Sharpeners	26	19	
Erasers	48	14	
Pens	52	58	
Crayons	34	47	

D

Write the digits 3, 4, 5 and 6 on small pieces of paper.

Using all 4 digits, arrange the numbers to make different multiplications.

☐☐ x ☐☐ = ☐☐☐   ☐☐☐ x ☐ = ☐☐☐

[3] [4]
[5] [6]

1. What is the largest answer you can make?

2. What is the smallest answer?

3. What answer is the nearest you can make to 1000?

Written division

Learning objective: to use written methods to divide H (hundreds) TU ÷ U

Some dividing you can do in your head as it links with multiplying. 48 divided by 6 is 8, which is easy if you know that 6 x 8 is 48. When you divide bigger numbers, you need to use a written method.

Remember!
If a number cannot be divided exactly it leaves a remainder.

What is 749 divided by 4?

Work out how many groups of 4 are in 749 and what is left over:

Method 1

```
     187 r 1
  4 )7 4 9
  - 4 0 0     (4 x 100)
    3 4 9
  - 3 2 0     (4 x 80)
      2 9
  -   2 8     (4 x 7)      749 ÷ 4 = 187 remainder 1
        1
```

Method 2

$$4)\overline{7^3 4\ ^29}\ \ \ 187\ r\ 1$$

$700 \div 4 = 100$
Carry 300 over to the tens.
$340 \div 4 = 80$
Carry 20 over to the units.
$29 \div 4 = 7$
The remainder is 1.

A Complete these divisions and write the answers with remainders.

1. $4\ 8\ 8 \div 3 \rightarrow$ _____ r __
    $$3)\overline{4\ 8\ 8}$$

2. $3\ 6\ 7 \div 5 \rightarrow$ _____ r __
    $$5)\overline{3\ 6\ 7}$$

3. $1\ 8\ 9 \div 4 \rightarrow$ _____ r __
    $$4)\overline{1\ 8\ 9}$$

4. $9\ 2\ 6 \div 4 \rightarrow$ _____ r __
    $$4)\overline{9\ 2\ 6}$$

DEFINITION

remainder: If a number cannot be divided exactly by another number then there is a whole number answer with an amount left over, called a remainder.

Use paper for written workings out.

B Draw a line to match each remainder to a division.

271 ÷ 6

315 ÷ 8

454 ÷ 5

608 ÷ 3

Remainder
1
2
3
4
5
6
7
8
9

149 ÷ 6

259 ÷ 9

359 ÷ 10

458 ÷ 9

398 ÷ 7

C

Eggs are collected every day and put into boxes of 6. Write how many full boxes can be made each day and how many eggs are left over to complete this chart.

Day of the week	Eggs collected	Number of	
		Full boxes (6 eggs)	Eggs left over
Monday	627		
Tuesday	572		
Wednesday	700		
Thursday	644		
Friday	683		
Saturday	594		
Sunday	735		

Rounding numbers

Learning objective: to use rounding and approximation to estimate calculations

We round numbers to make them easier to work with. It is useful for estimating approximate, or rough, answers.

> Decimal numbers can be rounded to the nearest whole number or tenth. Whole numbers can be rounded to the nearest 10, 100 or 1000. Round down if the digit is less than 5. Round up if the digit is 5 or more.
>
> To round decimals to the nearest whole number, look at the **tenth** digit.
>
> 4.**4**7 round down to 4
> 12.**7**5 round up to 13
>
> To round numbers to the nearest 10, look at the **units** digit.
>
> 2**4** round down to 20
> 8**5** round up to 90
>
> To round large numbers to the nearest 100, look at the **tens** digit.
>
> 68**2**8 round down to 6800
> 304**5**9 round up to 30500
>
> To round large numbers to the nearest 1000, look at the **hundreds** digit.
>
> 68**4**28 round down to 68000
> 304**6**59 round up to 305000

Tip: focus on the last 3 digits in each number.

A This chart shows some cities with a population of less than 1 million. Round each population to the nearest 100.

Town	Population	Nearest 100
Liverpool	469019	
Bradford	293717	
Sheffield	439866	
Derby	229407	
Birmingham	970892	
Nottingham	249584	
Bristol	420556	
Plymouth	243795	

B

Round each number to the nearest 100, then do the sum.

1. 415 + 388 → _____

2. 682 - 174 → _____

3. 597 - 489 → _____

4. 378 + 836 → _____

5. 2190 + 3675 → _____

6. 9251 + 4359 → _____

C

Round each of these to the nearest whole number of kilograms. Write the approximate total weights for each set.

1.	4.38 kg	2.97 kg	9.19 kg	Approx. total weight _____ kg
2.	9.49 kg	7.73 kg	3.64 kg	Approx. total weight _____ kg
3.	13.85 kg	12.55 kg	6.53 kg	Approx. total weight _____ kg
4.	19.09 kg	17.64 kg	8.47 kg	Approx. total weight _____ kg

D

Calculators can display lots of decimal places. We often round off numbers to 2 decimal places.

0.76398	→ rounds down to	0.76
3.42739	→ rounds up to	3.43

Round these to 2 decimal places.

1. 0.9286 _____   2. 7.0835 _____   3. 12.945 _____

4. 7.5881 _____   5. 2.9116 _____   6. 30.0794 _____

Decimal calculations

Learning objective: to use written methods to add and
subtract decimals

Some decimals you can add and subtract in your head, but other bigger
numbers will need a written method.

Adding and subtracting decimals is just like adding and subtracting whole numbers. Just
remember that the decimal point in the answer is in line with the decimal points above.

Example 1
What is 12.78 added to 37.41?

An approximate answer is 13 + 37 = 50

```
   12.78
 + 37.41
   50.19
    1 1
```

Example 2
What is 34.82 subtract 19.96?

An approximate answer is 35 – 20 = 15

```
  ²3 ¹³4 . ¹⁷8 ¹2
 - 1 9 . 9 6
   1 4 . 8 6
```

A Complete these additions.

1. 45.37
   + 22.46

2. 31.85
   + 52.91

3. 73.02
   + 18.79

4. 64.89
   + 20.62

B Complete these subtractions.

1. 77.86
   - 34.84

2. 90.52
   - 43.29

3. 65.19
   - 27.43

4. 58.03
   - 16.25

It is always a good idea to estimate an
approximate answer first, so you can
check your answer against your estimate.

C

Write the total measurements.

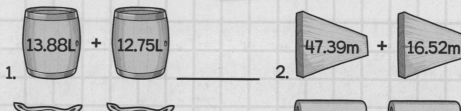

1. $13.88L + 12.75L$ _____

2. $47.39m + 16.52m$ _____

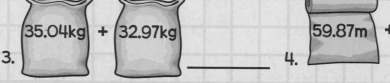

3. $35.04kg + 32.97kg$ _____

4. $59.87m + 21.36m$ _____

D

This chart shows the gymnasts' scores for four events. Using information from the chart answer the questions below.

Name	Horse Vault	Uneven Bars	Balance Beam	Floor Exercise
Eileen	18.10	19.16	18.96	19.36
Sandra	18.40	19.40	19.02	19.00
Nikki	19.16	18.89	18.66	18.96
Julie	19.19	19.26	19.13	19.20
Stacey	19.03	18.99	19.22	18.70

1. What is the difference between the Horse Vault scores of Sandra and Nikki?

2. What is the difference between the highest and lowest scores on the Uneven Bars?

3. Which two gymnasts have a difference of 0.4 in their Floor Exercise scores?

4. How many more points did Julie need on the Balance Beam to match the top score for this event?

5. The scores were each out of 20. How far from full marks was Nikki on the Balance Beam?

Simplifying fractions

Learning objective: to reduce a fraction to its simplest expression

With some fractions, it's hard to picture exactly what they mean.

The numerator (the number on the top) and the denominator (the number on the bottom) are both bigger than they need to be. Like this:

$$\frac{20}{25}$$

You can make fractions like this simpler and easier to understand if you can spot a number that divides both the numerator and denominator.

20 ÷ 5 = 4
25 ÷ 5 = 5

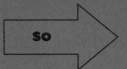 **so**

$\frac{20}{25}$ is the same as $\frac{4}{5}$

You must use the same number to divide the top and bottom of the fraction.

A Simplify these fractions.

1. 6 ÷ 3 =
   21 ÷ 3 =

 **so**

$\frac{6}{21}$ is the same as __

2. 9 ÷ 3 =
   15 ÷ 3 =

 **so**

$\frac{9}{15}$ is the same as __

3. 4 ÷ 2 =
   6 ÷ 2 =

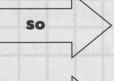 **so**

$\frac{4}{6}$ is the same as __

4. 12 ÷ 6 =
   18 ÷ 6 =

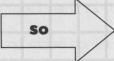 **so**

$\frac{12}{18}$ is the same as __

Hint: all even numbers divide by 2. All numbers that end with O divide by 10. And all numbers that end with O or 5 divide by 5.

B

Find the right number to simplify each fraction. Choose from **2, 5** or **10**.

1. 15 ÷ __ =

    40 ÷ __ =

    so → $\frac{15}{40}$ is the same as __

2. 14 ÷ __ =

    16 ÷ __ =

    so → $\frac{14}{16}$ is the same as __

3. 8 ÷ __ =

    12 ÷ __ =

    so → $\frac{8}{12}$ is the same as __

4. 20 ÷ __ =

    30 ÷ __ =

    so → $\frac{20}{30}$ is the same as __

C

Match each circle to a diamond.

$\frac{9}{18}$ $\frac{4}{5}$ $\frac{12}{15}$ $\frac{3}{4}$ $\frac{2}{3}$ $\frac{5}{6}$

$\frac{50}{60}$ $\frac{1}{4}$

$\frac{10}{15}$ $\frac{11}{33}$ $\frac{1}{2}$ $\frac{7}{28}$ $\frac{1}{3}$ $\frac{18}{24}$

Comparing fractions

Learning objective: to know how to compare and order a set of fractions

You may need to work out which fraction is bigger when you are comparing amounts.

For example, which would give you more of a cake: $\frac{2}{3}$ of it, or $\frac{3}{4}$ of the cake? This is tricky with different denominators.

Comparing fractions with the same denominator is easy:
For example, $\frac{4}{5}$ is bigger than $\frac{2}{5}$

$\frac{4}{5}$

$\frac{2}{5}$

To compare any fractions change them to equivalent fractions with a common denominator. This means they have the same denominator.

Example

Which is the larger fraction: $\frac{2}{3}$ or $\frac{3}{4}$? Find the equivalent fractions to $\frac{2}{3}$ and $\frac{3}{4}$ that have a common denominator.

$$\frac{2}{3} = \frac{4}{6} = \frac{6}{9} = \mathbf{\frac{8}{12}} \qquad \frac{3}{4} = \frac{6}{8} = \mathbf{\frac{9}{12}}$$

$\frac{9}{12}$ is larger than $\frac{8}{12}$

$\frac{3}{4}$ is larger than $\frac{2}{3}$

$\frac{3}{4} > \frac{2}{3}$

A Complete these to make a chain of equivalent fractions.

1. $\frac{1}{3} = \frac{\square}{6} = \frac{3}{\square} = \frac{\square}{12} = \frac{5}{\square} = \frac{\square}{\square}$

2. $\frac{1}{4} = \frac{2}{\square} = \frac{\square}{12} = \frac{4}{\square} = \frac{\square}{20} = \frac{\square}{\square}$

3. $\frac{1}{2} = \frac{\square}{4} = \frac{3}{\square} = \frac{\square}{8} = \frac{5}{\square} = \frac{\square}{\square}$

4. $\frac{2}{3} = \frac{4}{\square} = \frac{\square}{9} = \frac{8}{\square} = \frac{\square}{15} = \frac{\square}{\square}$

DEFINITION

denominator:
The bottom number of a fraction. Example: $\frac{2}{3}$

B Write < or > or = between each pair of fractions.

Use your completed equivalent fractions chains from Exercise A to help you change them to equivalent fractions.

1. $\frac{2}{3}$ $\frac{1}{2}$ 2. $\frac{1}{4}$ $\frac{1}{3}$

3. $\frac{2}{3}$ $\frac{4}{5}$ 4. $\frac{4}{5}$ $\frac{1}{2}$

< means less than.
> means more than.

C Draw a line and join each of these fractions to its correct place on this number line.

0   0.5   1

| $\frac{1}{10}$ | $\frac{3}{4}$ | $\frac{9}{10}$ | $\frac{2}{5}$ | $\frac{1}{5}$ | $\frac{7}{10}$ | $\frac{6}{10}$ | $\frac{1}{2}$ | $\frac{3}{5}$ | $\frac{1}{4}$ | $\frac{3}{10}$ | $\frac{4}{5}$ |

D Put each group of fractions in order starting with the smallest.

1. $\frac{1}{4}$ $\frac{3}{8}$ $\frac{1}{2}$ $\frac{10}{16}$

2. $\frac{1}{6}$ $\frac{1}{3}$ $\frac{3}{4}$ $\frac{6}{12}$

DEFINITION

numerator:
The top number of a fraction.
Example: $\frac{3}{5}$

37

Equivalents

Learning objective: to find equivalent percentages, decimals and fractions

When something is part of a whole, it can be displayed as a fraction, decimal or percentage.

Look at this grid.
25% of the grid is red.

$\frac{5}{20} = \frac{25}{100} = 25\%$

25% is the same as $\frac{1}{4}$.

Look at these methods for converting between fractions, percentages and decimals:

Per cent to decimal

Divide the percentage by 100

Example: 60% is the same as 0.6

Decimal to per cent

Multiply the decimal by 100

Example: 0.25 is the same as 25%

Per cent to fraction

Write the percentage as a fraction out of 100 and then simplify

Example: 40% is $\frac{40}{100}$, which is the same as $\frac{2}{5}$

Fraction to per cent

Write the fraction as a decimal and then multiply by 100

Example: $\frac{3}{4}$ is 0.75 which is the same as 75%

A Use the methods shown above to change these fractions and decimals to percentages.

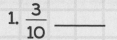

Turn to page 10 for revision on decimals.

1. $\frac{3}{10}$ _____   2. $\frac{1}{5}$ _____   3. $\frac{7}{100}$ _____   4. $\frac{11}{50}$ _____

5. 0.8 _____   6. 0.1 _____   7. 0.65 _____   8. 0.12 _____

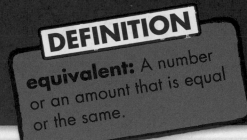

DEFINITION

equivalent: A number or an amount that is equal or the same.

 B Write the missing digits to complete these.

1. $\frac{1}{2}$ = 0._____ = 50%

2. $\frac{1}{4}$ = 0.25 = _____%

3. $\frac{1}{20}$ = 0.05 = _____%

4. $\frac{2}{\boxed{}}$ = 0.4 = 40%

5. $\frac{17}{50}$ = 0._____ = 34%

6. $\frac{7}{10}$ = 0.7 = _____%

 C Write the fraction and percentage shown by the shaded part of each shape.

1.

2.

3.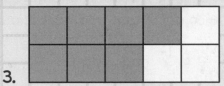

4.

5.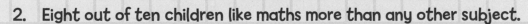

6.

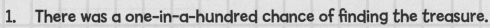

D Write the percentages for each of these headlines.

1. There was a one-in-a-hundred chance of finding the treasure.

There was a _____% chance of finding the treasure.

2. Eight out of ten children like maths more than any other subject.

_____% of children like maths more than any other subject.

3. Four in five people read our newspaper!

_____% of people read our newspaper!

4. Our football team won sixteen of their last twenty matches.

Our football team won _____% of their last twenty matches.

39

Percentages

Learning objective: to find percentages of whole number quantities

Percentages are simply fractions out of 100. 'Per cent' means 'out of 100' and the percentage sign is %.

We often need to work out percentages of amounts.
For example, what is 20% of 60 metres?
In examples like this, 'of' means multiply, so this is 20% x 60.
Look at these two methods to work this out.

Method 1

If you can multiply fractions, change the percentage to a fraction and work it out:

$$20\% = \frac{20^1}{100^5} = \frac{1}{5} \quad \text{and} \quad 60m = \frac{60}{1}$$

$$\frac{1}{5} \times \frac{60}{1} = \frac{60^{12}}{5^1} = 12m$$

Method 2

The quick method is to use 10% to work it out. 10% is 1/10, which is the same as dividing a number by 10:

10% of 60 is 6.

So, 20% of 60m is double that: 12m

A

Write these percentages as fractions in their lowest terms.

For example: $30\% = \frac{30}{100} = \frac{6}{20} = \frac{3}{10}$

1. 40% □ → □ → □

2. 80% □ → □ → □

3. 25% □ → □ → □

'Lowest terms' means using small numbers.

DEFINITION

percentage: This is a fraction out of 100, shown with a % sign.

B

These are the marks that Joseph scored in some maths tests. Change them all to percentages to work out which test he scored highest in and which was his lowest score.

Test	Score	Percentage	Test	Score	Percentage
1	$\frac{7}{10}$		4	$\frac{21}{25}$	
2	$\frac{18}{20}$		5	$\frac{38}{50}$	
3	$\frac{4}{5}$				

C

Write these amounts.

1. 10% of 70cm = _____

2. 30% of 90km = _____

3. 20% of 20 litres = _____

4. 40% of 30kg = _____

5. 50% of 70ml = _____

6. 25% of 80m = _____

7. 10% of 600g = _____

8. 50% of 400mm = _____

You can revise percentages and fractions on page 38.

D

This chart shows different percentages of each length. Complete the chart by writing in the missing lengths.

	50%	25%	10%	40%	5%
60m	30m				3m
50m		12.5m			
300m				120m	
250m			25m		

Proportion

Learning objective: to solve simple problems involving proportions of quantities

Finding the proportion of an amount is the same as finding the fraction of the whole amount. A proportion can be written as a fraction.

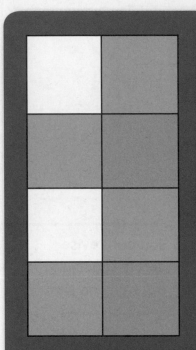

What proportion of the tiles are white?
When you look at the proportion of an amount, it is the same as finding the fraction of the whole amount.
There are 8 tiles altogether, 2 of them are white, so 2/8 of the tiles are white.
This means that the proportion of white tiles is 1 in every 4, or 1/4.

Two quantities are in direct proportion when they increase or decrease in the same ratio.
For example, if 3 apples weigh 300g, what is the weight of 15 apples?
This is 5 times the number of apples, so it is five times the weight: 300g x 5 = 1500g (or 1.5kg).

A Look at these tile patterns. What proportion of each of the patterns is blue?

1. ____   2. ____   3. ____   4. ____   5. ____   6. ____

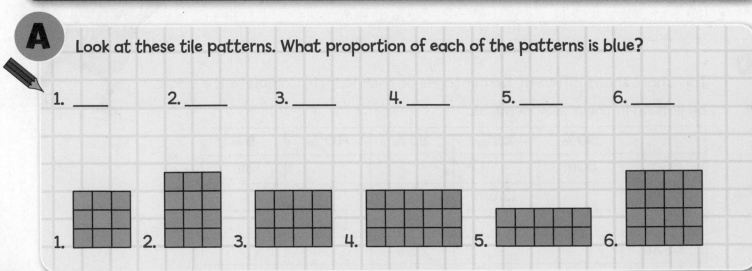

1.   2.   3.   4.   5.   6.

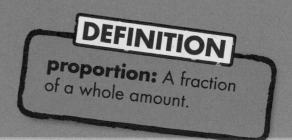

B

Complete these tables showing the proportion of fruit in juice drinks.

The fruits are measured in fifths. The proportion of fruit stays the same in each table.

1.

Pineapples	Oranges	Total
1	4	5
2	8	
	20	
8		
10		

2.

Bananas	Peaches	Total
2	3	5
4	6	
	18	
16		
		50

C

In these recipes the amount of each ingredient is given as a proportion of the total weight.

Write the missing weights of each ingredient in these two recipes.

1. **600g Carrot and walnut cake**

1/4 butter   150g

1/3 flour   200g

1/6 grated carrots   _____g

1/10 sugar   _____g

1/12 beaten eggs   _____g

1/15 walnuts   _____g

2. **360g Chocolate chip cookies**

1/2 flour   _____g

1/4 butter   _____g

1/6 sugar   _____g

1/12 chocolate chips   _____g

D

What weight of ingredients are needed for a 1.2kg carrot and walnut cake?

butter _____g

flour _____g

grated carrots _____g

sugar _____g

beaten eggs _____g

walnuts _____g

2D shapes

Learning objective: to describe the properties of polygons

Polygons are straight-sided, closed shapes. Quadrilaterals are any shapes with 4 straight sides.

Learn the properties of these different polygons.

Number of sides		Name	Number of sides		Name
3		Triangle	6		Hexagon
4		Quadrilateral	7		Heptagon
5		Pentagon	8		Octagon

Learn the properties of these different quadrilaterals.

Square
- 4 equal sides
- 4 right angles

Rectangle
- 2 pairs of equal sides
- 4 right angles

Rhombus
- 4 equal sides
- opposite angles equal
- opposite sides parallel

Parallelogram
- opposite sides are equal and parallel

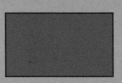

Kite
- 2 pairs of adjacent sides that are equal

Trapezium
- 1 pair of parallel sides

A

Count the sides and write the name for each shape.

1. _____

2. _____

3. _____

4. _____

5. _____

6. _____

2D means two-dimensional. Am I a 2D shape?

B

Name each of these quadrilaterals.

1. _____

2. _____

3. _____

4. _____

5. _____

6. _____

C

Complete these sentences by writing <u>always</u>, <u>sometimes</u> or <u>never</u>.

Look at the shapes on these two pages to help you.

1. A rectangle _____ has 4 right angles.

2. An octagon _____ has 7 sides.

3. The opposite sides of a parallelogram are _____ parallel.

4. The sides of a square are _____ equal.

5. A triangle _____ has a right angle.

6. The sides of a rhombus are _____ the same length.

45

Angles

Learning objective: to calculate angles in straight lines and triangles

The amount by which something turns is an angle.
Angles are measured in degrees (°). There are 360° in a circle.
These are some special angles to remember:

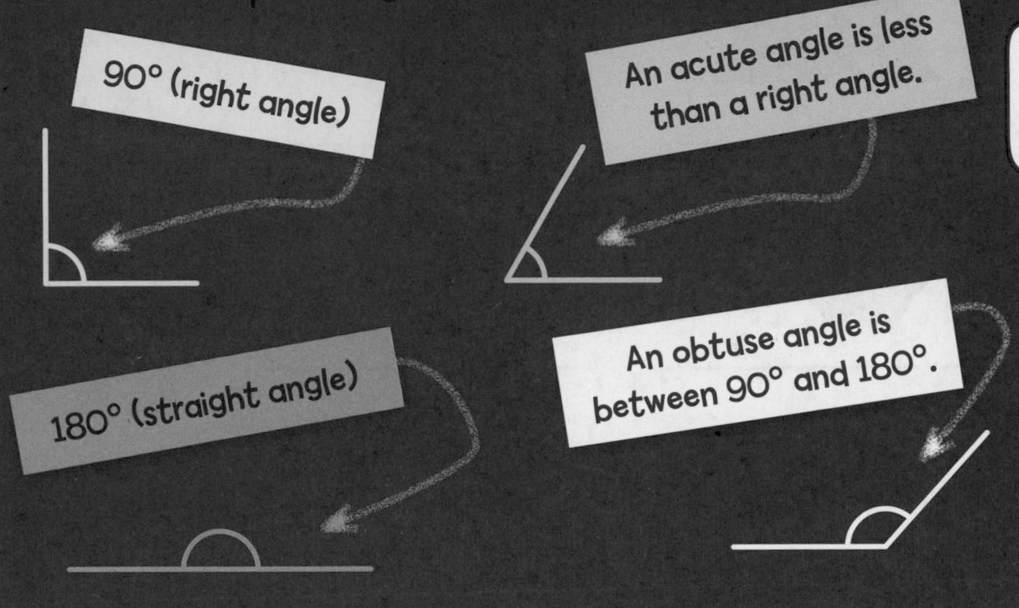

90° (right angle)

An acute angle is less than a right angle.

180° (straight angle)

An obtuse angle is between 90° and 180°.

A device called a protractor can be used to measure angles.

A Write the correct number next to the name of each angle in the chart.

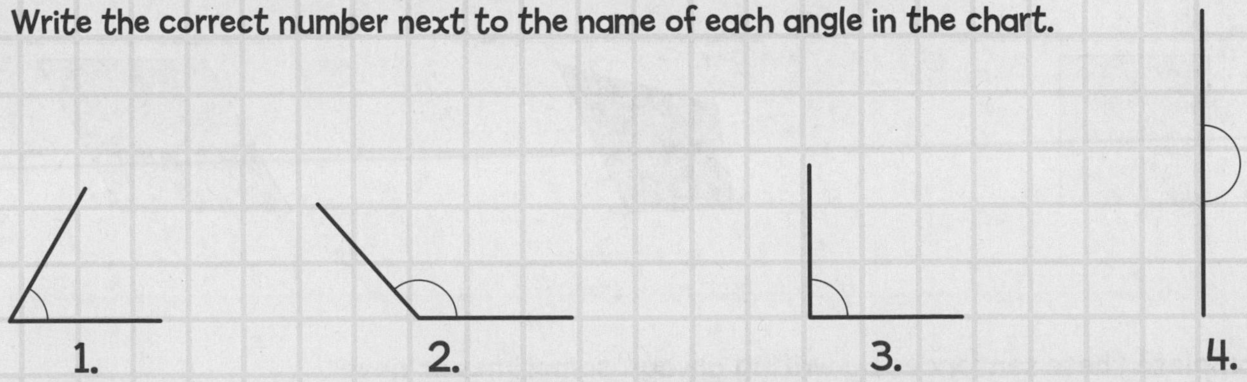

1.   2.   3.   4.

Straight angle	
Acute	
Obtuse	
Right angle	

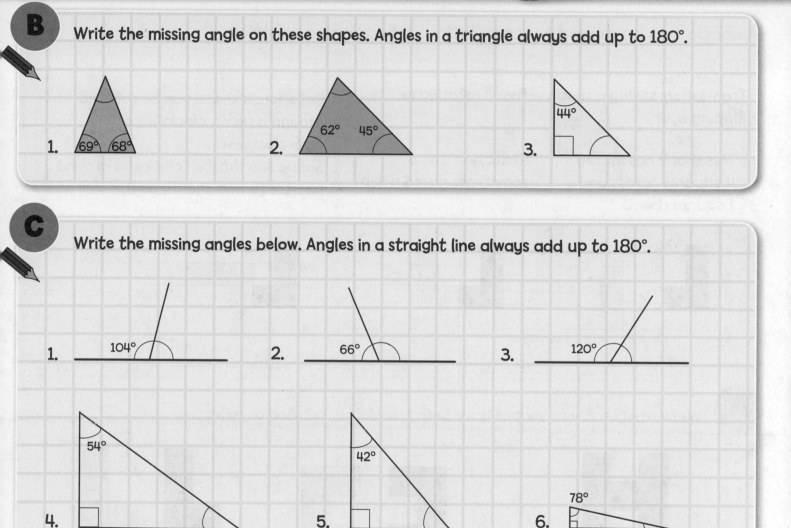

DEFINITION

angle: The amount by which something turns.

B Write the missing angle on these shapes. Angles in a triangle always add up to 180°.

1. 69° 68°

2. 62° 45°

3. 44°

C Write the missing angles below. Angles in a straight line always add up to 180°.

1. 104°

2. 66°

3. 120°

4. 54°

5. 42°

6. 78°

D Write the two missing angles on these.

1. 60°

2. 45°

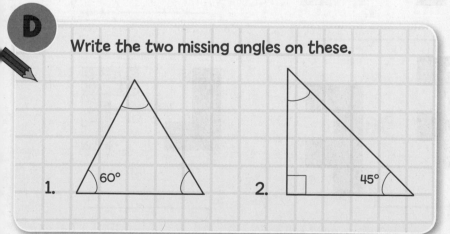

Remember that a right angle always measures 90°.

47

Moving shapes

Learning objective: to draw shapes on grids after translation, reflection or rotation

A shape can be moved by translation, reflection or rotation.

Translation: sliding a shape without rotating or flipping over.

This shape has moved 4 squares across and 1 square down.

Reflection: this is sometimes called a 'flip'.

Rotation: a shape can be rotated around a point, clockwise or anti-clockwise.
Shape A is rotated clockwise around point X to become shape B.

Point X

A Write whether these shapes have been translated, rotated or reflected.

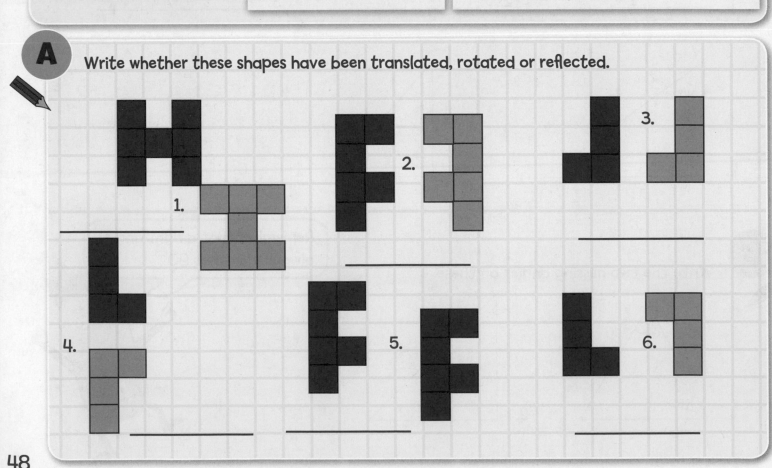

1. _____

2. _____

3. _____

4. _____

5. _____

6. _____

DEFINITION

clockwise: Moving in the same direction as the hands of a clock.

DEFINITION

anti-clockwise: Moving in the opposite direction to the hands of a clock.

B

Repeat these shape tiles to design a larger pattern.

Decide whether to rotate, reflect or translate each tile.

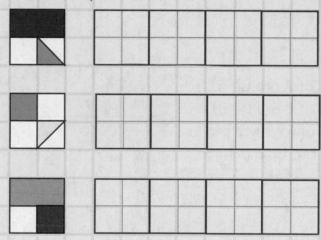

Can you make a symmetrical pattern?

C

Copy this tile and repeat it 10 times.

Use it to make a pattern of translated, rotated or reflected tiles.

Design your own tile and explore the patterns you can make.

Coordinates

Coordinates are used to show an exact position of a point on a grid.
Two numbers from the x and y axes show the position.

Look at the graph.

The coordinates of A are (2, 5)
The coordinates of B are (4, 3)
Coordinates are always written in
brackets separated by a comma.

The number on the
horizontal x axis is written
first, then the vertical y
axis. You can remember this
because x comes before y in
the alphabet!

A

DEFINITION

axis: The horizontal or
vertical line on a graph.
Plural is **axes**.

1. A, B and C are corners of a rectangle. What
are the coordinates of the fourth corner?

2. P, Q and R are corners of a parallelogram.
What are the coordinates of the
fourth corner?

DEFINITION

vertices: The corners of 3D shapes, where edges meet. Singular is **vertex**.

B Look at how each of these triangles has moved. Write the coordinates of the vertices of both triangles for each of them.

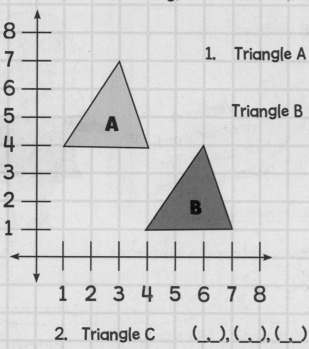

1. Triangle A   (1, 4), (3, 7), (4, 4)

Triangle B   (_,_), (_,_), (_,_)

2. Triangle C   (_,_), (_,_), (_,_)

Triangle D   (_,_), (_,_), (_,_)

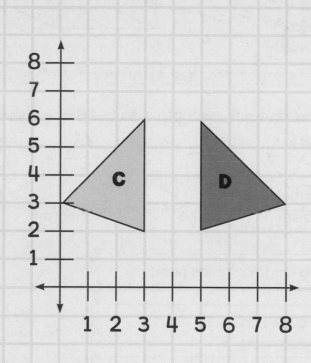

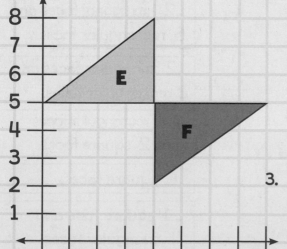

3. Triangle E   (_,_), (_,_), (_,_)

Triangle F   (_,_), (_,_), (_,_)

3D shapes

Learning objective: to describe the properties of 3D shapes

A solid shape has three dimensions: height, length and width.

Solid or 3D shapes are made up of faces, edges and vertices (corners).

A cuboid has 6 faces, 12 edges and 8 vertices.

An edge is where two faces meet.

A face is a flat surface of a solid.

Vertex is another word for corner. The plural is vertices.

What shape is a cereal box?

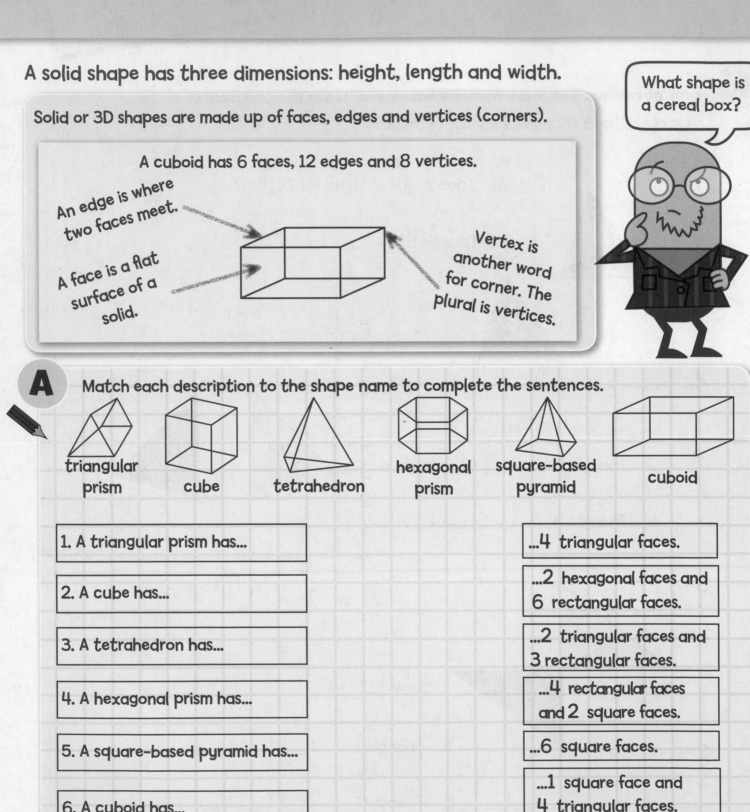

A Match each description to the shape name to complete the sentences.

triangular prism

cube

tetrahedron

hexagonal prism

square-based pyramid

cuboid

1. A triangular prism has...

2. A cube has...

3. A tetrahedron has...

4. A hexagonal prism has...

5. A square-based pyramid has...

6. A cuboid has...

...4 triangular faces.

...2 hexagonal faces and 6 rectangular faces.

...2 triangular faces and 3 rectangular faces.

...4 rectangular faces and 2 square faces.

...6 square faces.

...1 square face and 4 triangular faces.

DEFINITION

faces: The flat sides of a solid shape.

edge: Where two faces of a solid shape meet.

Prisms

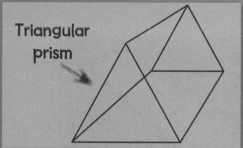

Triangular prism

Prisms have rectangular faces, with the shape of the end face giving each prism its name.

Cuboids and cubes are special types of prism.

Pyramids

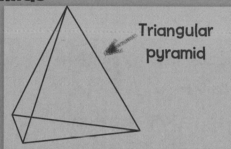

Triangular pyramid

The shape of the base gives each pyramid its name. The triangular faces of a pyramid all meet at a point.

Another name for a triangular pyramid is a tetrahedron.

B

Sort these shapes into prisms and pyramids. Complete the table below.

A

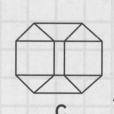

B

C

D

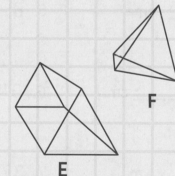

E

F

G

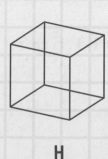

H

	A	B	C	D	E	F	G	H
Prism	✔							
Pyramid								

Measuring length

Learning objective: to convert units of length and measure lines accurately

We measure length using kilometres, metres, centimetres and millimetres.

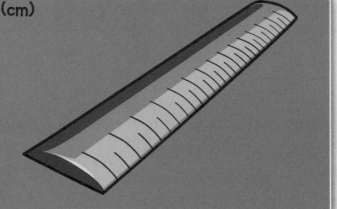

10 millimetres (mm) = 1 centimetre (cm)

100 centimetres = 1 metre (m)

1000 metres = 1 kilometre (km)

2.8cm = 2cm 8mm = 28mm

3.45m = 3m 45cm = 345cm

6.5km = 6km 500m = 6500m

To measure the length of lines accurately you may need to use millimetres.

A Complete these.

1. 58 mm = _____ cm

2. 10.67 m = _____ cm

3. 910 cm = _____ m

4. 13.5 cm = _____ mm

5. 8.3 km = _____ m

6. 94 mm = _____ cm

7. 3700 m = _____ km

8. 14.6 cm = _____ mm

Your work on decimals on page 10 will help you with these conversions.

B Use a ruler to measure the length of each line accurately in millimetres.

1.

4.

2.

5.

3.

6.

C The perimeter of a shape is the distance all around the edge.
These shapes are all regular, so each side is the same length.

Measure the length of one side of each shape in
millimetres. Use this measurement to work out
the perimeter of each shape.

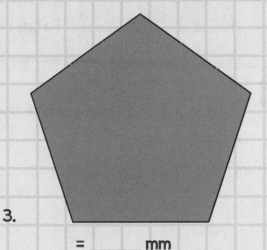

1.

= _____ mm

2.

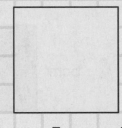

= _____ mm

3.

= _____ mm

4.

= _____ mm

Use millimetres when you
need to measure something
accurately.

Area

Learning objective: to be able to calculate the area of a shape

The area of a shape is the amount of surface that it covers.

The area of a rectangle or square can be calculated by multiplying the length by the width.

4cm

6cm

6cm x 4cm = 24cm²

The area of shapes made from rectangles can be found by working out the area of each part.

4cm

4cm

3cm

2cm

3 x 4 = 12cm²
2 x 4 = 8cm²
Total area = 20cm²

Area is measured in square units, such as square centimetres (cm²) and square metres (m²).

A

Calculate the area of each of these.

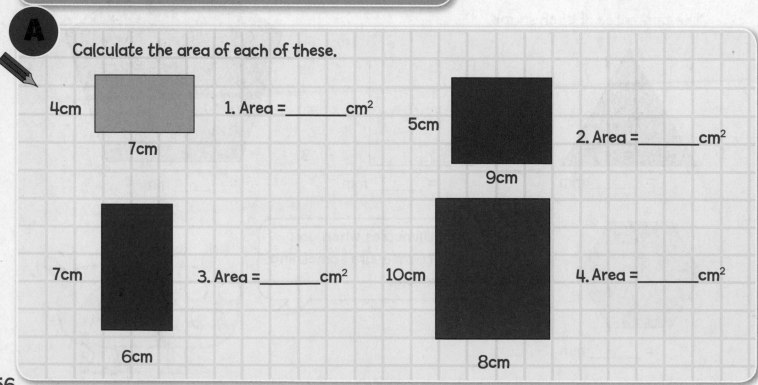

4cm

7cm

1. Area =_____cm²

5cm

9cm

2. Area =_____cm²

7cm

6cm

3. Area =_____cm²

10cm

8cm

4. Area =_____cm²

Remember!
The shapes below are not drawn to actual size.

B Write the area for each of these shapes.

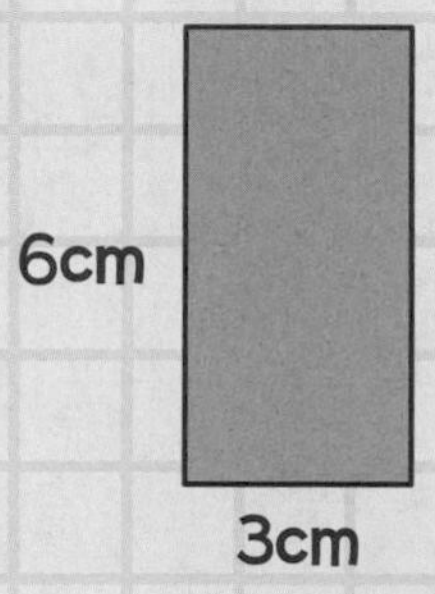

6cm
3cm

1. Area =_______cm²

2cm
5cm

2. Area =_______cm²

4cm
4cm

3. Area =_______cm²

5cm
3cm

4. Area =_______cm²

C Calculate the area of these shapes. Work out the area of each rectangle within the shape first.

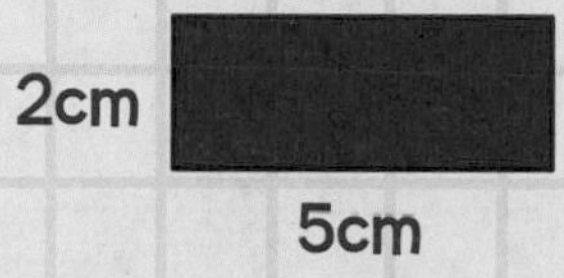

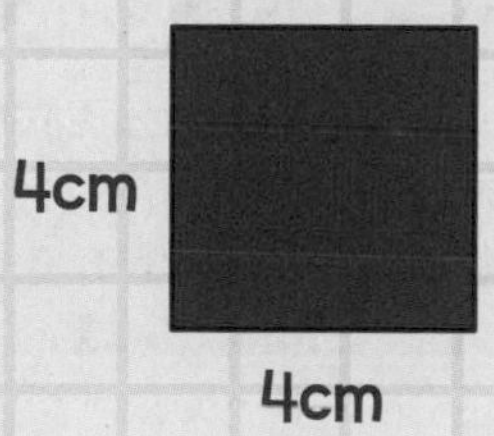

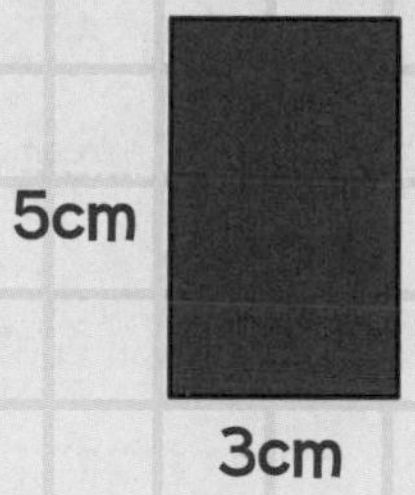

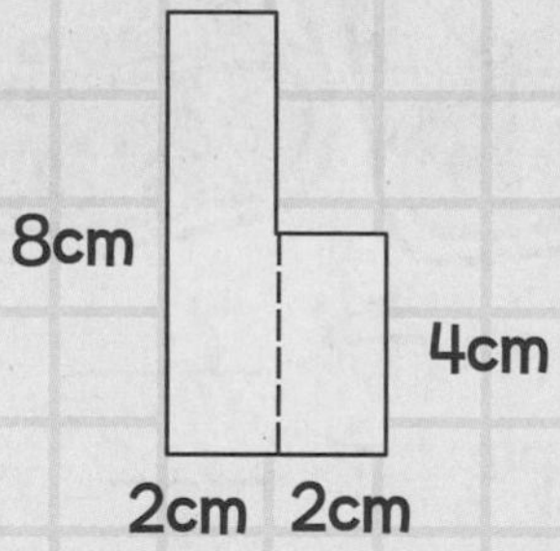

8cm
4cm
2cm
2cm

1. Area =_______cm²

5cm
3cm
2cm
1cm
2cm

2. Area =_______cm²

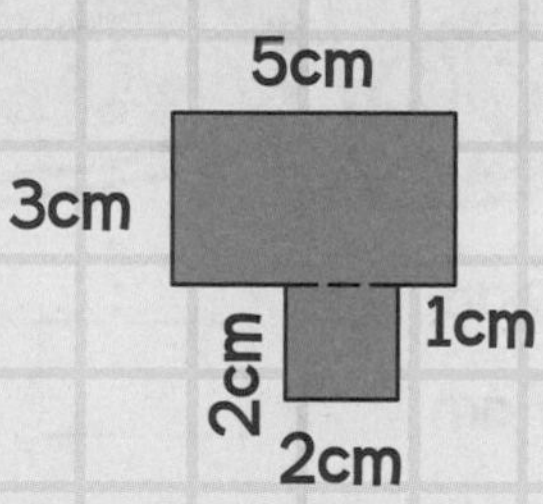

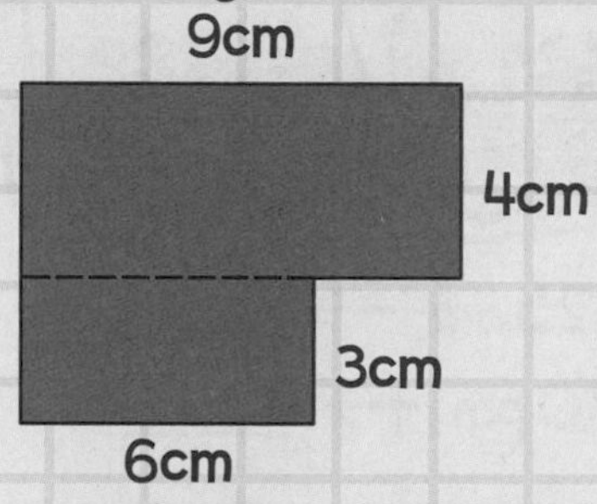

9cm
4cm
3cm
6cm

3. Area =_______cm²

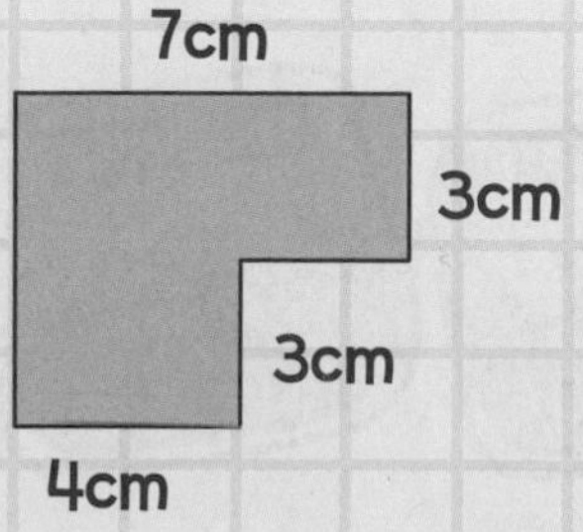

7cm
3cm
3cm
4cm

4. Area =_______cm²

3cm
2cm
3cm
4cm
9cm

5. Area =_______cm²

8cm
2cm
4cm
4cm
2cm
4cm
2cm

6. Area =_______cm²

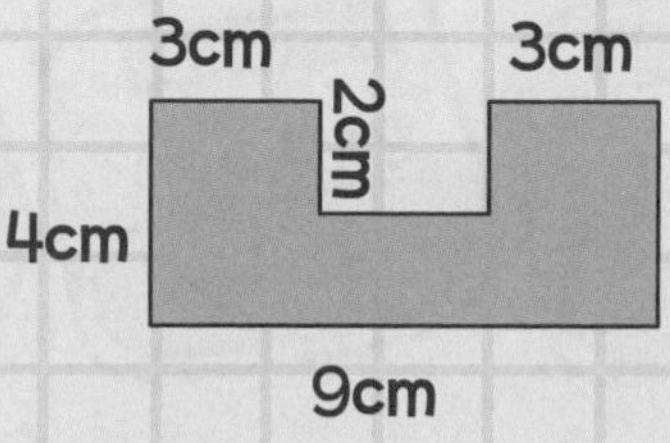

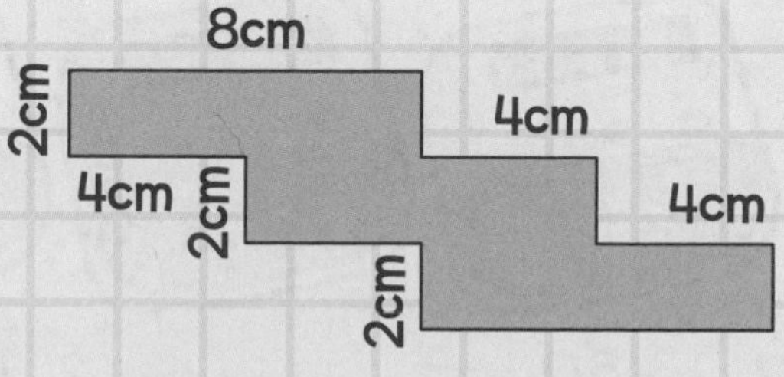

24-hour clock

Learning objective: to read the time using 24-hour clock notation

Timetables and digital watches often use the 24-hour clock.

This line compares 12-hour time and 24-hour time.

| 12 midnight | 1am | 2am | 3am | 4am | 5am | 6am | 7am | 8am | 9am | 10am | 11am | 12 noon | 1pm | 2pm | 3pm | 4pm | 5pm | 6pm | 7pm | 8pm | 9pm | 10pm | 11pm | 12 midnight |

| 00 | 01 | 02 | 03 | 04 | 05 | 06 | 07 | 08 | 09 | 10 | 11 | 12 | 13 | 14 | 15 | 16 | 17 | 18 | 19 | 20 | 21 | 22 | 23 | 24 |

24-hour time carries on after 12 midday to 13:00 rather than going to 1.00pm. For afternoon and evening times just add 12 to each time to change from 12-hour to 24-hour time.

6.30am → 06:30   11.40am → 11:40

6.30pm → 18:30   11.40pm → 23:40

A Write these times as 24-hour clock times.

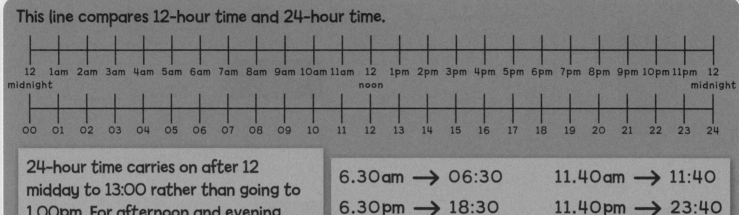

10.25 am   9.55 am   7.00 pm   4.30 pm   9.47 am   5.25 pm

1. 10.25am → __:__   2. 9.55am → __:__   3. 7.00pm → __:__
4. 4.30pm → __:__   5. 9.47am → __:__   6. 5.25pm → __:__

B Write these times as 12-hour clock times, using am and pm.

13:50   11:08   09:22   23:10   15:59   21:34

1. 13:50 → __.__   2. 11:08 → __.__   3. 09:22 → __.__
4. 23:10 → __.__   5. 15:59 → __.__   6. 21:34 → __.__

C

Write these same times in two lists, showing the times as both 24-hour and 12-hour times.

11.35am

Event	12-hour time	24-hour time
Alarm wake up	7.00am	07:00

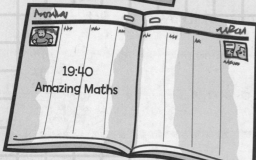

19:40 Amazing Maths

taxi 7.15pm

14:18

Meet for coffee 10.00am

D

6th July, 1989 at 11.45pm was a very special time.

It could be written as:

23:45 6.7.89!

What was special about 8.10pm on 20th October 2010?

_____

Work out some other special dates and times.

Find out about the date and time when you were born!

Data

Averages are middle scores or the most common numbers.
There are three main types of average: mean, mode and median.

> When working out the median and there is an even amount of numbers, you take the two middle numbers, add them together and divide by two.

Look at this example to compare the three types of average.
This chart shows the goals scored by the players in a football team.
Does Sam score above the average number of goals for the team?

Player	Sam	Brent	Jason	Ali	Carl
Goals scored	8	4	8	6	9

Mode is the most common number.
2 players scored 8 goals so that is the mode.

Median is the middle number when listed in order - 4, 6, 8, 8, 9.
8 is the median number of goals.

For the mean add the numbers and divide the total by the number of items in the list.
4 + 6 + 8 + 8 + 9 = 35   35 ÷ 5 = 7
So the mean average is 7 goals.

Sam is an above-average goal scorer compared with the mean average,
and at the average for the mode and median.

A

A packet of fruit-drops is divided into piles of different flavours.

grape (purple)   = 3   lemon (yellow)   = 4   strawberry (pink)   = 7
orange (orange) = 4   lime (green)   = 8   raspberry (red)   = 4

1. Which is the most common amount of sweets of the same flavour? _____

   Is this the mean, mode or median? _____

2. If the piles of sweets were put in order of size, which size pile would be in the middle?

   _____

   Is this the mean, mode or median? _____

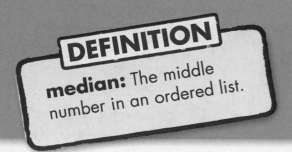
B

These are the heights of a group of five children.

| Ben: 140cm | Sam: 130cm | Eve: 140cm | Amy: 150cm | Jon: 190cm |

1. What is the mode height?

2. What is the median height?

3. What is the mean height?

4. How many children are above the mean average height?

5. Which child is at the mean average height?

6. Another child joins the group. Her height is 120cm. What is the mean average height for the group now?

Remember!
Mode is the most common number.

C

These are the hand-spans for a group of 10 children.

A hand-span is measured from the tip of the little finger to the tip of the thumb.

| 10cm | 8cm | 12cm | 9cm | 8cm | 10cm | 13cm | 11cm | 9cm | 10cm |

1. Median: _____   2. Mode: _____   3. Mean: _____

Challenge

Read this graph and find the median, mode and mean averages of the number of hours of TV watched each day in one week.

hours: 10, 8, 6, 4, 2, 0

Mon Tue Wed Thur Fri Sat Sun

4. Median: _____   5. Mode: _____   6. Mean: _____

61

Probability

Learning objective: to describe and predict outcomes using the language of chance

We can use a probability scale to show how likely an event is to happen.

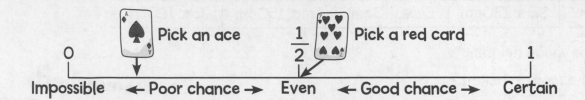

Pick an ace $\frac{1}{2}$ Pick a red card

0 ————————————————————————————— 1

Impossible ← Poor chance → Even ← Good chance → Certain

Method 1

Even chance, or evens, is an equal chance of something happening as not happening. We also say a 1 in 2 chance, 1/2 chance or a 50:50 chance.

Example: In a pack of playing cards there is an even chance of picking a red card.

Method 2

Dice experiments are useful for testing probabilities.

On a normal die, the probability of throwing a 2 is 1 in 6 or 1/6. That is because there is only one number 2 on the die out of a possible six numbers.

O means something will never happen. 1 means something will definitely happen.

A

These ten playing cards are shuffled and placed face down. Choose from the statements at the bottom to show the probability of turning over these cards.

1. a multiple of 2
2. a diamond
3. a multiple of 5

4. a number greater than 6
5. the queen of diamonds
6. the 9 of diamonds

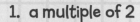

Impossible   Poor chance   Evens   Good chance   Certain

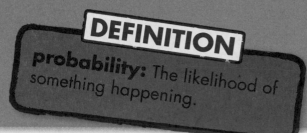

B Using a die, write the chance of throwing each of these.

Choose one of the following probabilities ➔   1 in 2   1 in 3   1 in 6

1. a six _____

2. an even number _____

3. a multiple of 3 _____

4. a number greater than 4 _____

5. a number less than 4 _____

6. a one _____

C Colour the correct number of beads in this bag to match these probabilities.

- There is a 50:50 chance of picking out a red bead from the bag.
- There is a 1 in 6 chance of picking out a blue bead from the bag.
- There is a 1/4 chance of picking out a green bead from the bag.
- It is impossible to pick out a yellow bead from the bag.
- There is a 1 in 12 chance of picking out a black bead from the bag.

How many of each colour are there?

1. _____ red beads

2. _____ green beads

3. _____ blue beads

4. _____ black beads

5. _____ yellow beads

Spelling tips

Learning objective: to know about different spelling methods

There are lots of things you can do to help with your spelling.

Learn words in groups. For example:

bright   fright   might   sight

Look, say, cover, write, check:

- look at the word
- say it out loud
- cover it with one hand
- write it without looking
- check it

Did you get it right?

Look for words within words, or words that have a common root. For example:

sign   signal   signature

Keep a spelling log of difficult words. For example, any with silent letters, such as:

knife   comb   cupboard

Break longer words into syllables. For example:

information = in/form/a/tion

Use a mnemonic. For example:

'Necessary' has one coffee with two sugars (there are one c and two s's in the word).

Say the word as it is spelt.

Learning the short words first will help you to spell the longer words later.

A

Look at the words below. Can you see any short words within them? Write the short words next to the long words.

caterpillar   cat pill ate ill pillar   supermarket _____

television   _____   subway   _____

cupboard   _____   basketball   _____

wardrobe   _____   crossword   _____

Some words, called homophones, sound the same but are spelt differently. For example:

| bus fare | fire grate | horse's rein |
| fair ground | great fun | rain water |

DEFINITION

mnemonic: A method to help you remember something, e.g. 'i' comes before 'e' except after 'c'.

syllable: The beats in a word are syllables. Words with only one beat are monosyllabic.

B

Read the passage below. Cross out any wrong spellings and write the correct spellings above.

On Saturday, we tuck the train into town. We usually go bye car because Mum

says the train fair is two deer, but she agrees it's much faster bye train.

We even had a drink on the train, witch we can't do in the car! We didn't

knead to pay four parking either so I think the train was cheeper in the end!

Spelling plurals

Nouns (people, places and things) can be either singular or plural.

For example:

one dog (singular)

two dogs (plural)

Remember!
To make most words plural, you just add an 's'.

Learning the rules will help you to spell plurals.

A

1. To make some nouns plural, you just add an 's'. Add an 's' to the end of these nouns to make them plural.

   banana___   girl___   boy___   day___   star___

2. To make some other nouns plural, you add 'es'. Write 'es' at the end of these nouns to make them plural.

   potato___   bus___   box___   dish___
   watch___   dress___   tomato___   brush___
   bench___   glass___   wish___   volcano___

Remember!

When nouns end in 'ch', 'sh', 's', 'ss' or 'x' add 'es' to make them plural. When a noun ends in 'o' we also usually add 'es'.

DEFINITION

singular: A singular word indicates that there is just one thing.

plural: A plural word indicates that there is more than one thing.

B

1. When a noun ends in an 'f' sound, drop the 'f' and write 'ves'. Write these nouns as plurals.

   leaf > lea _____   knife > kni _____   calf > cal _____

2. When a noun ends in a consonant followed by a 'y', drop the 'y' and write 'ies'. Have a go at these.

   baby > _____   butterfly > _____   pony > _____
   story > _____   party > _____   lady > _____

   Some plurals don't follow the rules. You will need to learn these separately.

   mouse > mice   tooth > teeth   man > men

3. Write the plurals for these tricky nouns. You can use a dictionary to help you.

   goose > _____   sheep > _____   deer > _____
   foot > _____   child > _____   woman > _____

Prefixes and suffixes

Learning objective: to learn about prefixes and suffixes

A prefix is a letter (or group of letters) added to the beginning of a word.
A suffix is a letter (or group of letters) added to the end of a word.

A

1. **Add the missing prefix or suffix. Tele means 'far away'. Auto means 'by itself'.**

Another word for your signature	auto _____
A long tube with a lens at the end	tele _____
Something that works by itself	_____ matic
Another word for car	auto _____
Something that allows you to speak to someone far away	tele _____
Your own life story, written by you	_____ biography

2. **Sometimes a prefix is added to change the meaning of a word. If the prefix 'anti' means 'not', what do you think these words mean? Write your definitions.**

anti-ageing _____

anti-bacterial _____

anti-freeze _____

B

Which of these things would you expect to find in toothpaste? Circle your answer.

anti-ageing cream

an anti-bacterial
ingredient

anti-freeze

So, 'anti-' isn't the same as 'aunty' then?!

C

Add the missing suffixes. Choose from 'cian' or 'ist'. Then write a definition for each one.

Word	Meaning
magician	Someone who performs magic tricks
pian _____	
chem_____	
beauti_____	
electri_____	
musi_____	
politi _____	
biolog_____	

A suffix can change a word from singular to plural, but can also change a verb (an action word) into a noun.

verb		**noun**
paint		painter
dance		dancer

D

Add the suffix 'er' to change these verbs into nouns.

verb	noun
sing	
garden	
teach	
climb	
walk	
play	

Punctuation

We use punctuation to show the reader how words should be spoken and to help them understand the text.

Commas tell readers to pause and take a moment to understand what a sentence is about. Put a comma after each item of a list. Put a comma after a group of words that belong together. Never put a comma before the word 'and' in a list.

A Write the missing commas in these sentences.

> When Superboy whispered a secret word his school jumper became a long shiny red cloak and his spectacles morphed into a mirrored black mask. His super-human powers enabled him to climb vertical walls scale rooftops sense danger and bring wrong-doers to justice.

Exclamation marks (!) are used to signal surprise, excitement or humour.

B Read the passage below and write in exclamation marks or full stops where they are missing.

> All of a sudden, the rock door split open and a dark figure sprang out It was the Evil Weevil, Superboy's deadliest enemy Weevil eyed him menacingly for a second and lunged forward with a blood-curdling battle cry

Don't over-use exclamation marks!

DEFINITION

punctuation marks: These are commas, full stops, exclamation marks, apostrophes, etc – the punctuation we use to make our writing clearer to the reader.

exclaim: This means 'to cry out'. Hence we say 'exclamation mark'.

Question marks (?) are used to signal a question.

C Write a question mark at the end of the sentences where questions are asked.
If a sentence is not a question, you can use either a full stop or an exclamation mark.

How was Superboy going to defeat the Evil Weevil Was he cunning and clever enough to

outwit him Everyone knew that the Weevil was a wimp really but he was a scary wimp, all

the same What would happen if Superboy failed Would the Earth be plunged into another

inter-planetary war

Remember!

Sentences that ask questions usually begin with Who, What, When, Where, How, Why or Can.

Speech marks are drawn around any words that are spoken.

D Write the speech marks in the dialogue below.

So, Superboy, we meet at last, the Weevil sneered. It's a shame we don't have time
to strike up a friendship! Ha, ha, ha! The Weevil laughed at his own feeble joke.

I wouldn't worry, Weevil, replied Superboy. You'll have plenty of time to make friends
with the cockroaches you'll meet in the state planetary prison!

Remember!

- Speech marks open at the start and close at the
  end of the words spoken.
- All punctuation for the spoken sentence goes inside
  the speech marks.
- Start a new paragraph for each new speaker.

More punctuation

Learning objective: to learn to use apostrophes, colons and ellipses

Apostrophes are a form of punctuation that can be used in two different ways.

When an apostrophe is used to shorten a word it is known as a contraction. Apostrophes can also be used to show possession.

Examples of contractions:	Examples of possessive words:
do not = don't	Sally's shoes
can not = can't	The dog's dinner
we are = we're	My sister's dress

Do you know the difference between possessive apostrophes and contractions?

A

In the sentences below, circle the apostrophes that shorten words and underline the apostrophes that show possession.

1. I can't find it. It's gone!
2. That's my friend's house.
3. It's Toni's book.
4. Where's Mrs Dale's class?
5. They'll be late for school.
6. We're going to Gina's party.

B

Write these contractions in full.

can't > _____   they'll > _____

it's > _____   where's > _____

that's > _____   we're > _____

With an apostrophe, 'it's' is a contraction that means 'it has' or 'it is'. Without an apostrophe, 'its' is used to show possession.

Examples of contractions with 'it's':	Examples of the possessive 'its':
I think it's been raining.	The dog buried its bone.
It's warm outside today.	The sweet stuck to its wrapper.
It's nearly lunchtime.	The door fell off its hinges.

In plural nouns, possessive apostrophes come after the 's'.

C Put possessive apostrophes in these sentences.

1. The clowns car fell apart. (one clown)
2. The clowns car fell apart. (two clowns)
3. The dogs owner went to the Pooch Parlour. (one dog)
4. The dogs owner went to the Pooch Parlour. (two dogs)
5. The girls rabbit ran away. (one girl)
6. The girls rabbit ran away. (two girls)
7. The mans sunglasses were expensive. (one man)
8. The mens sunglasses were expensive. (two men)

Remember!
There are some exceptions to the rules.
For example:
children = children's
men = men's

DEFINITION

contraction: A word formed by omitting (leaving out) or combining some of the sounds of a longer phrase.

These are some of the other punctuation marks you are likely to come across:

Pauses are marked with ellipses...
"I'd like a burger, fries and... ummm, an ice cream, please," said Emma.

Ellipses can also be used to show that words are missing.
"He left the room, banged the door...and went out."

Lists start with a colon:
The meal deal includes: a whopper burger, mega-fries and a drink.

Clauses and conjunctions

Learning objective: to learn about clauses and conjunctions

A clause is a group of words with a subject (a noun) and a verb. A sentence always has at least one clause.

> For example:
>
> | The show ended. (one clause) | 'the show' = noun | 'ended' = verb |
> | The audience clapped loudly. (one clause) | 'the audience' = noun | 'clapped' = verb |

Two or more clauses can be joined in a sentence.

> For example:
>
> The show ended and the audience clapped loudly.
>
> Or:
>
> The audience clapped loudly when the show ended.

Can you spot the nouns and the verbs?

The words 'and' and 'when' are called conjunctions. A conjunction is a word that is used to join together the parts of a sentence.

A

Join these sentences using conjunctions from this list:

so   and   that

1. It was lucky for me. It was not going to be a problem.

   It was lucky for me _____ it was not going to be a problem.

2. The sun was burning hot. We had to put on lashings of sunscreen.

   The sun was burning hot _____ we had to put on lashings of sunscreen.

3. She clicked her fingers. The little dog began to dance.

   She clicked her fingers _____ the little dog began to dance.

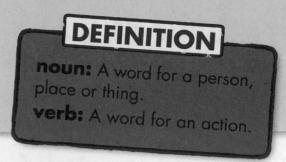

Connectives are words that link together ideas, sentences and paragraphs.

Here are some examples of connectives:

first   next   finally   consequently   later   suddenly   except
meanwhile   however   when   but   after   although   also   and

B

Underline the connectives.

First, we went to the Tower of London to see the Crown Jewels. Next, we saw Big Ben

and, after lunch, we had a great time at the London Dungeon. Although it rained for

most of the day we didn't really notice, except when we finally got back to the bus

station and had to wait ages for the bus to come... in the rain!

C

Choose from these connectives to complete the passage below:

next   first   lastly   but   then

_____ we went on the Ghost Train. It wasn't as scary as we thought it was going to
be. _____ _____ we went on the Rocky Coaster and that was terrifying! We
thought we were going to go flying off the track! _____ we got a real soaking on the
Log Flume and the Crazy Rapids. _____ we had a ride on the Angry Camel and it was
so funny that we couldn't stop laughing.

Pronouns

Learning objective: to understand how to use pronouns

A noun is a person, place or thing. A pronoun is used to replace a noun so that you don't have to repeat it.

For example, the second of these two sentences uses the pronoun 'he' instead of repeating 'Mr Parker':

Mr Parker is strict but Mr Parker makes us laugh.
Mr Parker is strict but he makes us laugh.

A

Choosing from the list below, change the underlined nouns to pronouns. Cross out the noun and write the pronoun above it.

I	me	you	he	him	she
her	we	us	they	them	it

1. Mr Parker gave Class 5 a detention so <u>Class 5</u> missed their playtime.

2. Our class won the merit prize so <u>our class</u> are going on a trip to the zoo.

3. Chris is team captain because <u>Chris</u> is the best at football.

4. Katie loves swimming so <u>Katie</u> joined the swimming club.

5. I usually like history but today <u>history</u> was boring.

6. We watched a film about spiders because we were doing a topic on <u>spiders</u>.

Possessive pronouns show ownership (or possession).

B Complete the sentences by choosing possessive pronouns from the list.

mine   his   hers   yours   theirs   ours   its

1. It belongs to me. It's _____.
2. This belongs to you. This is _____.
3. The coats belong to them. The coats are _____.
4. The cat belongs to her. The cat is _____.
5. The dog eats the dinner that belongs to it. The dog eats _____ dinner.

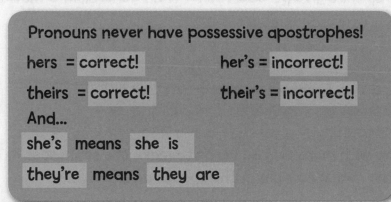

Pronouns never have possessive apostrophes!

hers = correct!   her's = incorrect!

theirs = correct!   their's = incorrect!

And...

she's means she is

they're means they are

C Write three sentences of your own using different pronouns.

1.

2.

3.

Verbs and adverbs

Learning objective: to learn how to use verbs and adverbs

Verbs and adverbs bring action and pace to your writing. Choose them carefully!

A Write the past tense for each of these verbs.

I draw   ⟶   I _____

I write   ⟶   I _____

I swim   ⟶   I _____

I catch   ⟶   I _____

I see   ⟶   I _____

I go   ⟶   I _____

Remember! A verb is an action word.

You can improve your writing by choosing verbs that give precise, rather than general, information.

For example:	
The giant ate the cakes.	(ate = general verb)
The giant gobbled up the cakes.	(gobbled = precise verb)

B Replace the underlined verbs below with more precise verbs to make the sentences more interesting for the reader. Write the new sentences in the spaces on the right.

1. The giant <u>walked</u> across the room.   1. _____

2. "Hubble, bubble, toil and trouble," <u>said</u> the witch.   2. _____

3. The elf <u>went</u> into the shop.   3. _____

4. The vampire <u>got</u> out of the coffin.   4. _____

5. The wizard <u>made</u> a potion.   5. _____

Adverbs usually answer questions, such as How? Where? or When?

For example:

The giant immediately gobbled up the sweets.   immediately = adverb

Here are some examples of adverbs:

really   easily   poorly   deeply   plainly

clearly   happily   angrily   badly   fiercely

Many adverbs end in -ly.

C Add an adverb to each sentence. Use your own ideas, or choose from this list:

quietly   carefully   suddenly   quickly   angrily   menacingly

1. The giant stomped _____ across the room.
2. "Hubble, bubble, toil and trouble," cackled the witch _____.
3. The elf sneaked _____ into the shop.
4. The vampire _____ leaped out of the coffin.
5. The wizard _____ concocted a potion.
6. The boy _____ snatched the wand.

DEFINITION

adverb: An adverb gives more meaning and explanation to the verb.
past tense: The form of the word that tells us something happened in the past.

Remember!
An adverb can change the meaning of a sentence.

Adjectives and metaphors

Learning objective: to learn how to use adjectives, metaphors and similes

An adjective describes a noun.

Clever use of adjectives can make your writing more exciting.

The adjectives in the second sentence tell the reader more about the bird and the nest.

For example:

The bird swooped down from its nest.

bird = noun   nest = noun   swooped = precise verb

The rare, golden-feathered bird swooped down from its rocky nest.

rare, golden-feathered, rocky = adjectives

A Make these sentences more exciting for the reader by adding adjectives. Write the new sentences on the lines below.

1. The car raced round the track.

   _____

2. The pony jumped the fence.

   _____

3. The chef cooked a meal.

   _____

4. The plane landed on the runway.

   _____

5. The artist painted a picture.

   _____

Describe one thing as if it really is something else and you are using a metaphor.

Example of a metaphor:
The moon is a silver mirror.

B Write down what you think these metaphors mean.

1. Joe's a sly fox! _____
_____

2. Jen's a rock. _____
_____

Describe one thing as if it is like something else and you are using a simile.

Examples of similes:
The giant's hands were like great shovels.
His feet were as big as boats!

C Write your own similes to complete these sentences about a terrible troll. The first one has been done for you.

1. His hair looked like. . . a bird's nest.
2. His teeth were like. . . _____
3. His nose was like a. . . _____
4. His toes were like. . . _____

D Complete these well-known similes.

1. As hard as. . . _____
2. As strong as an. . . _____
3. As weak as a. . . _____

4. As white as a. . . _____
5. As cold as. . . _____
6. As red as a. . . _____

81

Word play

You can brighten up your writing or add humour by playing with words.

A A proverb is a well-known saying that expresses a comment on life.

Explain what you think each proverb means.

1. Practice makes perfect. _____

_____

2. A stitch in time saves nine. _____

_____

3. Look before you leap. _____

_____

4. Don't look a gift horse in the mouth. _____

_____

5. Too many cooks spoil the broth. _____

_____

Remember!
Many proverbs are also metaphors.

An idiom is something people often say, where the message is different from the actual meaning of the words.

B Find out what these idioms mean and write a definition for each one.

1. I'm feeling under the weather. _____

2. He had egg on his face. _____

3. It's raining cats and dogs. _____

4. We're cooking on gas. _____

Onomatopoeia is when a word echoes the sound it is describing.

For example:

pop!

clash!

smash!

bash!

C

Complete each sentence with an appropriate onomatopoeia. Choose from:

pop   fizzed   buzzed   squelched   thud   smashed   crashed

1. The balloon burst with a loud _____.
2. The glass _____ onto the floor.
3. My feet _____ in thick mud.
4. The heavy door closed with a _____.
5. The bees _____ around the flowers.
6. The waves _____ onto the rocks.
7. The drink _____ in the can.

DEFINITION

onomatopoeia: A word that actually sounds like the word it is describing.
collective noun: A word for a group of things, e.g. choir, team, pack.

D

Do some research and complete these collective nouns. Choose from the list below:

cows   dolphins   geese   wolves   lions   birds   bees

Remember!
Using a collective noun is a more interesting way of writing about a group of animals.

1. A gaggle of _____
2. A pack of _____
3. A pride of _____
4. A herd of _____
5. A flock of _____
6. A swarm of _____
7. A school of _____

First, second and third person

There are three main types of writing – first, second and third person.

Writing in the first person means using the pronouns I, my, mine and we.

First person is usually used for:
- diaries and letters
- personal accounts of events, activities and visits
- autobiographies
- stories told by the leading character

Writing in the second person means addressing the reader directly, using the pronoun you.

Second person is usually used for:
- advertisements
- instructions and directions
- discussion texts

Writing in the third person means using the pronouns he, she, it and they.

Third person is usually used for:
- novels and stories
- information texts
- news reports

Look for examples of first, second and third person text in comics, magazines and newspapers.

DEFINITION

first person: When someone writes about himself or herself.

second person: When someone writes to address you as the reader.

third person: When someone writes about someone or something else (e.g. he, she, it, they).

A

Read the three pieces of writing below and decide whether they are written in the first person, second person or third person. Underline the pronouns to help you decide. Then write 1st, 2nd or 3rd in the box next to each extract.

1. Palm-fringed beaches and turquoise waters await you on this Caribbean dream holiday. You can enjoy five-star luxury with classic elegance at the Fabulossi Hotel for only £1,000 per person, including flights.

2. Emily felt betrayed. Lisa was her best friend. They'd been friends since they were four years old and at nursery together. But now she'd seen a note written on a page in Lisa's Pony Diary: 'Number one best friend: Becky. Number two best friend: Emily.'

3. Just when I thought it couldn't get any better, we scored again. It was a 3-0 hat-trick with only a minute left! Everyone around me went wild, including my dad. It was the best feeling ever!

B

Now rewrite the text from extract 2 in the first person.

_____

_____

_____

_____

_____

_____

Classic fiction

Learning objective: to learn how to extract information from a classic text

This is an extract from a book called **Treasure Island**. Read it twice, carefully.

... I was far less afraid of the captain himself than anybody else who knew him. There were nights when he took a good deal more rum and water than his head would carry; and then he would sometimes sit and sing his wicked, old, wild sea-songs, minding nobody.

But sometimes he would call for glasses round, and force all the trembling company to listen to his stories or bear a chorus to his singing. Often I have heard the house shaking with "Yo-ho-ho, and a bottle of rum", all the neighbours joining in for dear life, with the fear of death upon them, each singing louder than the other to avoid remark.

For in these fits he was the most over-riding companion ever known. He would slap his hand on the table for silence all round. He would fly up in a passion of anger at a question, or sometimes because none was put, and so he judged the company was not following his story. Nor would he allow anyone to leave the inn till he had drunk himself sleepy and reeled off to bed.

Robert Louis Stevenson (1850–94)

This text is written in the first person.

DEFINITION

sea-song: A song that sailors might sing.
over-riding: A person who is extremely loud, bossy and forceful towards others.

A

Use the text on page 86 to answer these questions.

1.   Was the person telling the story afraid of the captain?

2.   What kind of person was the captain?

3.   What did he do when he drank too much?

4.   Why did everyone sing so loudly? Explain your answer.

5.   What made the captain angry?

6.   Why did he slap his hand on the table?

7.   Do you think the person telling the story knows the captain well?

Classic poetry

Learning objective: to read and understand a classic poem

This is an extract from a poem called **Upon a Snail**. Read it twice, carefully.

Upon a Snail

She goes but softly, but she goeth sure,
She stumbles not, as stronger creatures do;
Her journey's shorter, so she may endure
Better than they which do much further go.

She makes no noise, but stilly seizeth on
The flower or herb appointed for her food;
The which she quietly doth feed upon,
While others range, and glare, but find no good.

And though she doth but very softly go,
However slow her pace be, yet 'tis sure;
And certainly they that do travel so,
The prize which they do aim at, they procure.

John Bunyan (1628–88)

DEFINITION

goeth: goes
to endure: to keep going
stilly: quietly
seizeth: takes hold of
herb: green plant or leaf
doth: does
range: travel far
glare: stare searchingly
pace: speed
'tis: it is
procure: gain or win

For activities about writing poetry, see page 104 of this workbook.

A

Use the poem on page 88 to answer the following questions.

1. Which words in the poem suggest that it was written a long time ago?

2. What is the poet's name?

3. In what year did the poet die?

4. Write two words that rhyme in the poem.

5. What does the snail in the poem eat?

6. What does 'while others range, and glare, but find no good' mean?

7. What does the last verse mean?

Poetry: alliteration and rhyme

Learning objective: to be able to recognize alliteration and rhyme in a poem

Alliteration is when writers put words together that start with the same sound.

A Write the missing letters in the first verse of the poem below to complete the alliterations. Then have a go at writing two more verses. Draw a picture to illustrate each verse.

For example: The **S**nake **S**lowly **S**piralled around the branch.

1. _neaky _nake:
   _oftly _liding,
   _ecretly _pying.

2. _linky _nake:
   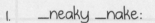
   _____

3. _leepy _nake:
   _____
   _____

1.

2.

3.

When words end with the same sound, we say that they rhyme. Poets use rhyme to make their poems more memorable and to give the words a pattern.

The Eagle

He clasps the crag with crooked hands;
Close to the sun in lonely lands,
Ringed with the azure world, he stands.

The wrinkled sea beneath him crawls;
He watches from his mountain walls,
And like a thunderbolt he falls.

Alfred, Lord Tennyson (1809–92)

DEFINITION

alliteration: Words that start with the same sound, e.g. fox, fire, phone.
rhyme: Words that end with the same sound 'rhyme', e.g. boat and coat, wing and ring.

B Read the poem and underline the rhymes. Then read it again and underline the alliterations. Copy the words below to make two lists. Can you add to the lists with words of your own?

Rhymes:

_____

_____

_____

_____

_____

_____

_____

Alliterations:

_____

_____

_____

_____

_____

_____

_____

Playscripts

Learning objective: to understand the layout of a playscript

This is an extract from a play. Read it twice, carefully, and take notice of the way in which it is written – for example, the stage directions are in italics.

Scene 1:
Last Day of Term
Classroom in 31st-century Britain.

Characters:
Narrator
Teacher: Number 1471
Robot Assistant: Bot

Narrator: It was the last day of term. Teacher 1471 and his robot assistant, Bot, were getting ready for the day ahead.

1471: *(yawning)* Good morning, Bot.

Bot: *(entering the date on the touch-screen learning wall)* Greetings, Sir, on this the three hundred and sixty-sixth day of term!

1471: Give out the books please, Bot.

Bot: Do you mean those curious, pre-computer-age page-turners, Sir? We haven't used those for over a thousand years!

1471: I know we haven't, but I thought we'd start with an ancient history lesson today!

A Rewrite the playscript as an ordinary story text, putting in speech marks and other punctuation. The first few sentences have been done to start you off.

It was the last day of term. Teacher 1471 and his robot assistant, Bot, were getting ready for the day ahead.

"Good morning, Bot," said 1471, yawning.

Speech marks can be used to break up long sections of speech.

For example, these sections of speech are rather long:

"Do you mean those curious, pre-computer-age page-turners, Sir? We haven't used those for over a thousand years!" **exclaimed Bot.**

"I know we haven't, but I thought we'd start with an ancient history lesson today!" **replied 1471.**

It sounds better to write:

"Do you mean those curious, pre-computer-age page-turners, Sir?" **asked Bot.** "We haven't used those for over a thousand years!"

"I know we haven't," **replied 1471,** "but I thought we'd start with an ancient history lesson today!"

Legends

A legend is a traditional story about a person or an event in history. It is based on truth, but retold to be more exciting. This is an extract from the legend **The Trojan Horse**. Read it twice, carefully.

The Trojan Horse

The Greeks and the Trojans had been at war for ten years. The Greeks were determined to rescue their queen, Helen, who had been kidnapped by Paris, the Trojan prince. But the Greeks could not break down the walls of Troy.

Odysseus thought up a plan. He ordered a huge wooden horse to be designed so that he and his soldiers could hide inside it. Then the Greek ships sailed away from Troy, leaving behind one man, Sinon, and the wooden horse. The ships lay in wait…

When the Trojans saw the Greeks sail away they thought they had won the war, but they were suspicious when they saw the horse. Sinon persuaded them that it would bring them luck.

So the Trojans dragged the horse into the city. That night they had a huge celebration until finally everyone fell asleep. Sinon released the door in the belly of the horse and Odysseus and his soldiers poured out. The Trojans were killed in their beds and the gates of Troy were opened to the Greeks, who had returned in their ships. Finally, Helen was rescued and Troy was destroyed.

A Use the text from the legend of the Trojan Horse on page 94 to answer these questions in complete sentences.

1. Why were the Greeks and the Trojans at war?

2. Was Odysseus a Greek or a Trojan?

3. Why did the Trojans believe the war was over?

4. How important was Sinon to the success of the plan?

5. Why did the Trojans celebrate that night?

6. Did Odysseus' trick work?

Odysseus (sometimes known as Ulysses) was king of Ithaca, in Greece. He was believed to be a clever and cunning leader.

Reports and information

Non-fiction is text that is based on fact. Encyclopedias, dictionaries and reference books are examples of non-fiction. This is an extract from a science report about jellyfish. Read it twice, carefully.

Jellyfish

Jellyfish are not fish, despite their name. They are fish-eating animals that float in the sea. They have soft bodies and long, poisonous tentacles that they use to catch their prey and protect themselves from predators.

There are many types of jellyfish. The smallest are just a few centimetres across. One of the biggest species lives in the Antarctic Sea. Its tentacles can reach up to 45 metres, or about half a football pitch!

One of the deadliest jellyfish is the Box Jelly. The venomous sting of this jellyfish can kill people. In Australia, the Box Jelly kills up to 65 people a year.

Most jellyfish tend to eat small creatures such as shrimps, plankton and microscopic fish. They wait for their prey to drift by, wrapping their tentacles around them and injecting them with a poison. But jellyfish themselves are vulnerable to predators and are eaten by creatures that don't fear their tentacles, e.g. turtles or other jellyfish.

Jellyfish have no brain, heart or bones, except a jaw! Jellyfish breathe in a different way to humans or fish. They have no lungs or gills. The walls of their body and tentacles are so thin that oxygen is able to pass directly from the water into their internal organs.

When you see jellyfish on the beach you wouldn't imagine there was so much to learn about them!

Answer these questions in full sentences.

1. Where is one of the biggest species of jellyfish found?

2. Which is one of the most deadly jellyfish?

3. What do jellyfish eat?

4. To which creatures are jellyfish prey?

Try doing some of your own research on another sea creature, and write a paragraph below explaining anything interesting you have found out.

Rewrite, in your own words, any information you find. Don't just copy the text.

DEFINITION

prey: An animal that is hunted by another animal for food.
predator: An animal that hunts another animal.

Explanation text

Writing that explains who, what, when, where, why and how is called explanation text. This is a piece of explanation text about how the Romans built their roads. Read it twice, carefully.

How were Roman roads built?

The Romans were famous road builders. Some of the roads they built are still being used today, over 2000 years later. So how did they build their roads to last this long?

First of all, they would look for the straightest route between two points. The trees and shrubs were cleared and a ditch 1 metre deep was dug. The ditch was filled with three layers.

The first layer, at the bottom of the ditch, was made up of big stones. This was to prevent the road from sinking.

On top of this, making up the second layer, they put small broken stones, pebbles, sand and cement.

For the third layer, they cut large, flat paving stones out of hard rock and set these tightly together in concrete to make the surface of the road. The road was slightly curved at the top so that rain water would drain off.

Finally, the edge of the road was lined with upright kerbstones. Major roads had ditches cut on each side.

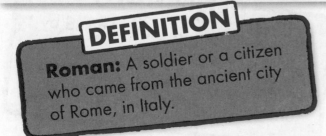

DEFINITION

Roman: A soldier or a citizen who came from the ancient city of Rome, in Italy.

Diagrams and charts are often drawn alongside explanation text to make the meaning clearer.

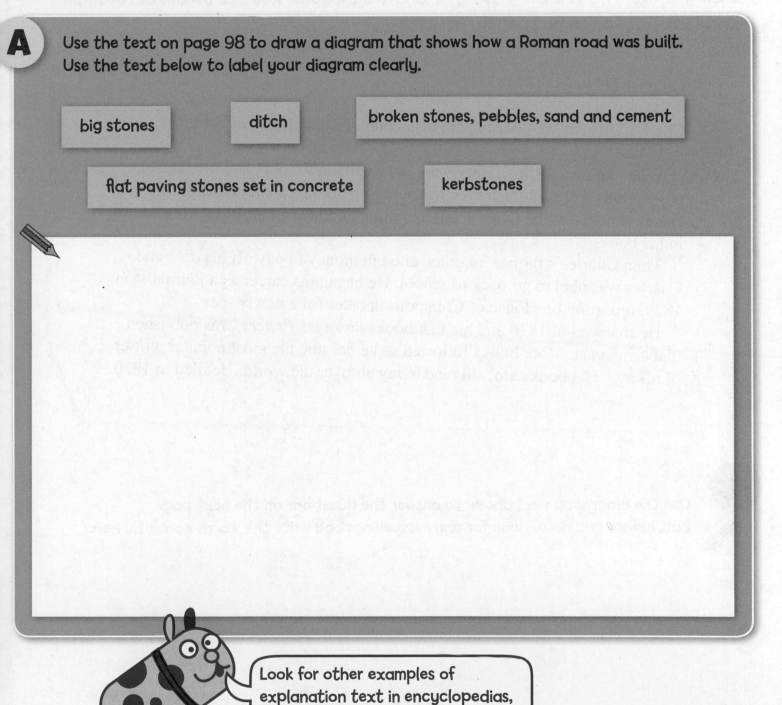

A Use the text on page 98 to draw a diagram that shows how a Roman road was built. Use the text below to label your diagram clearly.

big stones

ditch

broken stones, pebbles, sand and cement

flat paving stones set in concrete

kerbstones

Look for other examples of explanation text in encyclopedias, reference books and online.

Biography

A book, or a piece of writing, that is an account of a person's life is called a biography. This is a biography of Charles Dickens. Read it twice, carefully, and look out for some spelling mistakes!

Charles Dickens (1812–70)

Charles Dickens wos born near Portsmouth, England, on 7th February in 1812.

When he wos 12, his father wos sent to prison for debt and the family possessions were sold. Charles was sent to work in a shoe blacking factory. His experience at the factory was appalling and later he would write about it in his books.

Then Charles's farther inherited enough money to pay off his debt and Charles was abel to go back to school. He began his career as a journalist in 1829, reporting on House of Commons debates for a newspaper.

He married in 1836 and his first book, *Pickwick Papers*, was published that same year. More books followed as he became the most popular writter of his age. His books are still read today all over the world. He died in 1870.

A Use the biography text above to answer the questions on the next page. But, before you do so, look for any misspellings and write the words correctly here.

Use the biography text about Charles Dickens to answer these questions in complete sentences.

1. How old was Charles Dickens when he died?

2. Why do you think dates are important in a biography?

3. What was Charles doing on each of these dates? (Next to each date write some information taken from the text on page 100.)

   1812: _____

   1824: _____

   1829: _____

   1836: _____

   1890: _____

4. Write a short biography below of someone you admire or know well. Try to include some important dates.

Formal letters

This is a formal letter of complaint. Read it twice, carefully.

3 Park Road
Newtown
Cheshire
CH32 5RS
United Kingdom

Marco Martino
Manager
Excellenti Hotel
Naples
Italy

8th May 2014

Dear Mr Martino,

I am writing to complain about the lack of service and poor quality of the Excellenti Hotel.

Firstly, we spent the greater part of our two-week holiday waiting to be served in the restaurant. When our meals finally arrived each day, they were cold and inedible.

Secondly, we had booked a luxury family room with a sea view, but found ourselves in a cupboard that was not big enough to swing a cat in, although we had a wonderful view of the rubbish bins.

Thirdly, the swimming pool was more like an over-sized bathtub – hardly big enough for four guests, let alone the forty guests who were booked in at the hotel.

Finally, the cicadas made a deafening din, waking us up at dawn each day. No mention was made of these other noisy guests in the brochure.

I hope you agree that this is not the kind of service one would expect of the five-star Excellenti Hotel, and trust that you will offer us compensation for the disappointment this has caused us.

Yours sincerely,

I. M. Notamused

Mrs I. M. Notamused

A

Now have a go at answering these questions about the letter.

1. What do you think the word 'inedible' means?

2. Find an example of sarcasm in the letter and copy it here.

3. Underline the words in the letter used to connect the paragraphs (the connectives).

4. Circle an example of a metaphor.

5. Is there anything about the holiday that the manager could not have changed?

6. In which city was the hotel?

A formal letter is always laid out in the same way. Use the template on the right as a guide when you are writing a formal letter.

Write a short letter to the manager expressing the opposite viewpoint about the Excellenti Hotel.

Your address and the date

The person you are writing to and their address

Dear Mr/Mrs/Ms/Miss _____,

Use formal language, eg: I am writing ...

Write in the first person, using **I**, **my**, **mine** and **we**.

Yours sincerely,

_____

103

Writing poems

Learning objective: to write a poem based on a given structure

Fiction is writing that comes from your imagination. Poems, fairy tales, adventure stories and playscripts are all types of fiction.

A haiku is a traditional Japanese poem that has a total of 17 syllables arranged in three lines: 5, 7, 5.

For example:

Brilliant blue sky	Brill/i/ant/ blue/ sky
Trees dressed in emerald green	Trees/ dressed/ in/ em/er/ald/ green
Now that summer's here.	Now/ that/ summ/er's/ here.

'Dog' has one syllable, 'donkey' has two syllables and 'dinosaur' has three syllables.

A Have a go at completing this haiku about autumn.

_____ / _____ / _____ / _____ / sky

Trees _____ / _____ / _____ / _____ / _____ / _____

Now that autumn's here.

B Then try spring and winter following the same '5, 7, 5' haiku format.

_____

_____

_____

_____

_____

_____

A kenning is a kind of word puzzle or riddle. It is a way of talking about something without using its name.

Here are two examples:

Blood-sucker
People-biter
Loud-buzzer.

Noisy-barker
Tail-wagger
Bone-eater.

Can you work out what each kenning is about? When you think you know, check your answers at the bottom of the page!

C Try writing some kennings of your own below. Choose an animal or a familiar object. Test them out on a friend.

All good writers use their senses to describe what they can see or imagine.

D Use your senses to complete the senses poem below.

I'd love to taste:
A crunchy potato crisp, lightly sprinkled with sea salt and black pepper.
I'd love to see:
_____

I'd love to hear:
_____

I'd love to touch:
_____

I'd love to smell:
_____

Sentences and paragraphs

Learning objective: to rearrange sentence order and divide text into paragraphs

In good writing, the sentences don't all follow the same pattern.
If they did, the writing would sound dull.

> If you change the order of words in a sentence, you can keep your writing lively and interesting. Which of these word orders do you like best?
>
> 1. As the thunder crashed, Jack saw a tall tree looming up from the shadows.
>
> 2. Jack saw, as the thunder crashed, a tall tree looming up from the shadows.
>
> 3. Jack saw a tall tree looming up from the shadows, as the thunder crashed.

A

Find two different ways to rewrite each of the sentences below.
Use the same words but add any commas you need.

1. A crow, big and black, screeched in the darkness.
   _____
   _____

2. Jack, startled, held his breath.
   _____
   _____

3. He realized, with horror, a creature was creeping towards him.
   _____
   _____

4. A church bell rang close by, like some kind of terrible warning.
   _____
   _____

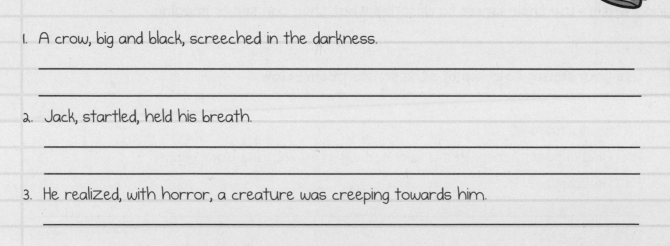

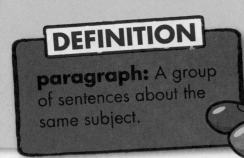

DEFINITION

paragraph: A group of sentences about the same subject.

Writers put sentences that are about the same subject into groups called paragraphs. It helps readers make sense of the writing.

Paragraph rules

- Group sentences together that are about the same idea, place, action or person.
- In a story, start a fresh paragraph when something new happens.
- Leave a blank line between paragraphs.
- Start a new paragraph about 2cm in from the margin, so it is easy to spot.

B

Below, the writing is squashed up into one paragraph, making it hard to read. It should be spread out into three paragraphs. Draw two vertical lines in two places where you think new paragraphs should start.

Jack started to run. He ran down the hill and along the hedge, looking for the gate. It was there somewhere, but in the dark, he just couldn't find it. He knew he didn't have much time. "I wonder where Jack is," said his mother, looking anxiously at the kitchen clock. "He's going to be late for his tea!" The thing on the hill lifted its head to gaze at the moon. It snuffled the cold, clear air. Then it let out a long, blood-curdling howl and lumbered after Jack.

C

In each of these paragraphs, there is one sentence in the wrong place. Underline the sentence that belongs in the other paragraph.

Jack's scrabbling fingers found the latch of the gate. It was rusty and stiff. He rattled it hard, but it wouldn't shift. Long, sticky drool slobbered from its jaws. He'd have to climb over instead.

Its breath came in clouds as it blundered down the hill. Great, stinking clouds, that smelled like rotting cabbage. He glanced anxiously over his shoulder. Its coarse black hair stood up stiffly, like spines.

Writing story settings

Learning objective: to recognize different settings and write a story setting

The setting is where and when a story takes place. Describing the setting can create mood and atmosphere.

A Draw lines to match the settings below to the appropriate stories on the right.

1. Fairytale castle or forest

2. School or home

3. Old house or graveyard at night

4. Remote or faraway place

5. Other planets

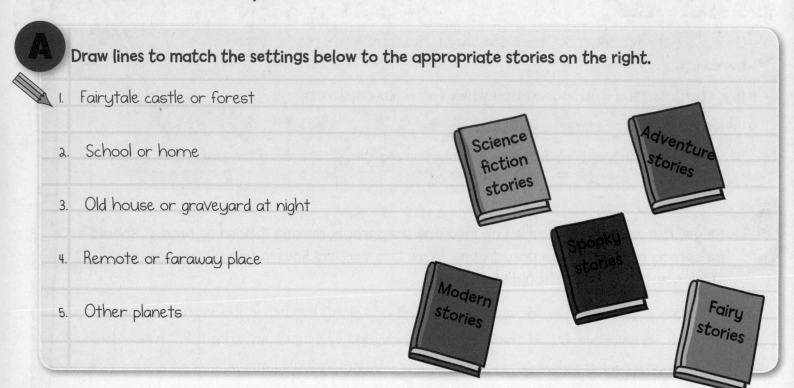

Science fiction stories

Adventure stories

Spooky stories

Modern stories

Fairy stories

B Read the passage below. Circle the words that tell you where and when this story is set.

The summer sun is high in the sky. The crashing waves break against my chest as I race towards them with my board. In front of me, I hear my friends shouting and I taste excitement in the salty air.

DEFINITION

atmosphere: This is the feeling you create for the reader. It can be scary, funny, mysterious and so on.

remote: A faraway, lonely place.

- Decide on where and when – think about the place and time of year. Will it be in the past, present or future? Will it be daytime or night-time?

- Describe what you can see, hear, feel, smell or taste.

- Draw a picture to help you imagine the scene.

Bells chime midnight

Moonlight casts a ghostly glow

Grey tombstones leaning over

A graveyard at night...

Hideous gargoyles watch

Shadows shiver in cold, dark, black corners

Drawing a spider diagram is a great way to plan a story setting.

Trees whisper and groan

C

Write a story setting below based on a graveyard at night. Use some of the words and ideas from the spider diagram above to help you – and add some ideas of your own.

Writing parables and ballads

A parable is a story that teaches a moral lesson. Many religious faiths have parables. For example, the Bible contains many parables told by Jesus.

Here is a summary of a parable called **The Good Samaritan**.

A man is attacked and robbed as he walks down the road. Many people pass by, but no one stops to help him. Eventually, a Good Samaritan comes along and helps the man.

 A Write a modern-day parable based on the story of The Good Samaritan. Think about the setting where your parable takes place. Who is the person in need of help? Who is your Good Samaritan?

A parable is similar to a fable, but a fable has animal characters instead of people. Both types of story have a moral.

A ballad is a song or poem that tells a story. It has short rhyming verses and often a chorus repeated after each verse.

B Read this ballad. Then fill in the missing rhyming words with words of your own.

Memories of a Norman Soldier

Will I be lucky or will I not
Succeed in helping with William's plot?
Men were facing me with death
My cheeks feel their icy _____.

Chorus:
It was a gory sight
The battle full of death and fright
To see the people suffer so
The victims of the deadly bow!

Now arrows are falling like _____
Surely the Saxons fight in vain
My arrows shoot in to the sky
Towards the enemy they _____.

Harold is now in clear view
In his direction the arrows _____
One has hit him in the _____
For now he shall surely die.

As I watch Harold _____
A tear comes to my weary eye
As I look at what we've done
It's a tragedy, but the war is _____!

By Holly and Natasha (age 11)

Writing instructions

Learning objective: to know how to write clear instructions

Instructions need to be written in a clear and concise way. Sometimes, when it is difficult to explain something in words, you can use a diagram as well.

How to draw a dog

What you need:
- paper
- pencil

What you do:
1. Draw a faint oval outline for the body and a smaller oval for the head.
2. Draw two small ovals for ears and four thin ovals for legs.
3. Within and on top of the oval outlines, draw more realistic dog-like features.
4. Then add details such as a nose, mouth, eyes, tail and spots.

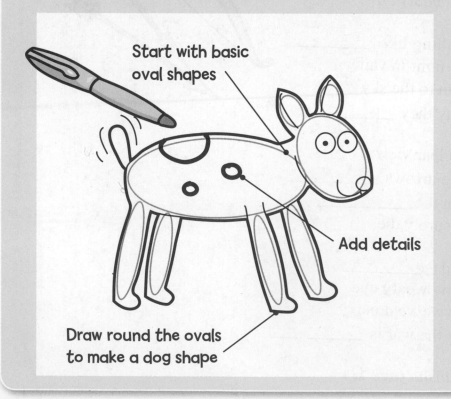

Start with basic oval shapes

Add details

Draw round the ovals to make a dog shape

Add labels and leader lines where necessary to explain your diagram.

DEFINITION

concise: Using as few words as possible to say something.

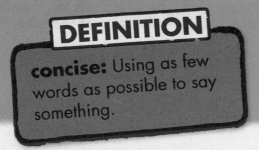

A craft project
- Write a list of what you are going to need.
- Number the separate points.
- Write step-by-step instructions.
- Draw a diagram if you think it would be helpful.

Remember!
Write in the present tense and second person, using the pronoun 'you'.

A Write a set of instructions explaining how to build a sandcastle with a moat.

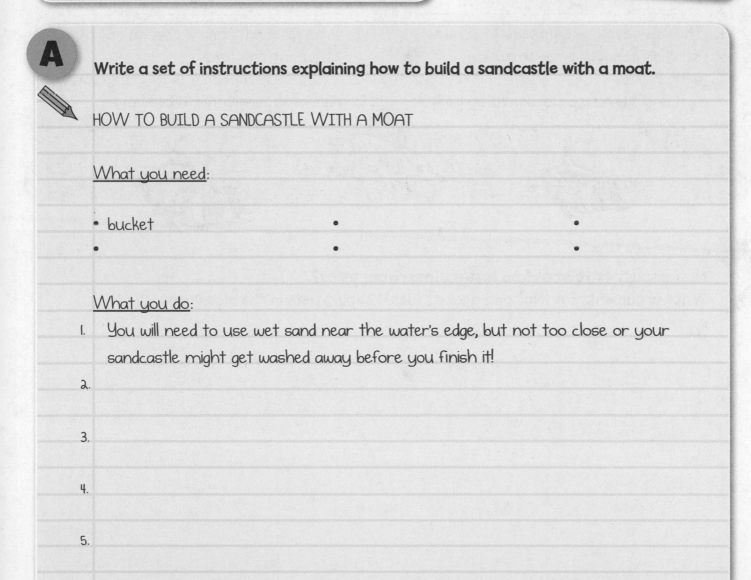

HOW TO BUILD A SANDCASTLE WITH A MOAT

What you need:

- bucket   •   •
- •   •   •

What you do:
1. You will need to use wet sand near the water's edge, but not too close or your sandcastle might get washed away before you finish it!

2.

3.

4.

5.

Writing a discussion text

Learning objective: to know how to write a discussion text

Discussion text can be used to bring together all the arguments for and against in a discussion.

Discuss: Is it cruel to keep fish in aquariums? Read the arguments on both sides.

Yes	No
1. The fish develop symptoms of stress. 2. Starfish can lose limbs when mishandled. 3. Fish don't like to be touched by people.	1. Vital research can be carried out by observing the fish. 2. Living in the ocean is more dangerous. 3. Fish kept in aquariums live longer.

A

Now discuss: **Is it cruel to have classroom pets?**
Write arguments for (No) and against (Yes) keeping pets in the classroom.

No

Yes

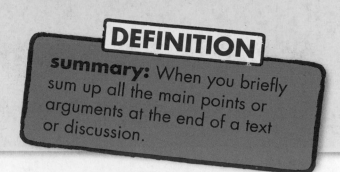
Connectives are used to link phrases together to make points in the discussion. The last paragraph summarizes the arguments and states the writer's point of view.

Discuss: **Is it cruel to keep fish in aquariums?** Read the discussion text below.

Many people say it is cruel to keep fish in public aquariums because the fish develop symptoms of stress. However, experts state that vital research is carried out by observing the fish. Others argue that fish don't like to be touched, and many starfish lose limbs when people mishandle them. On the other hand, many say the open ocean is a far more dangerous place and that fish kept in aquariums live longer.

In summary, there are valid arguments on both sides. On balance, I believe aquariums do more good than harm and their research is vital in helping us to learn about fish.

B Use your arguments for and against keeping classroom pets to write a discussion text in the space below. Read the example above to give you an idea of how to set out your arguments.

Writing to persuade

Learning objective: to understand how to write an advertisement

Advertising text (or 'copy') is used to try to persuade you to buy something.

> Advertising copy from the **Super Sandwich Company**:
>
> Our Super Sandwiches are home-made with special care using only the best local ingredients. You can't buy a healthier sandwich! And there are over 10 tasty fillings to choose from!

A Read the advertising copy above and choose three adjectives that describe a Super Sandwich.

1.
2.
3.

Design a package in the space below that will persuade people to buy a Super Sandwich.

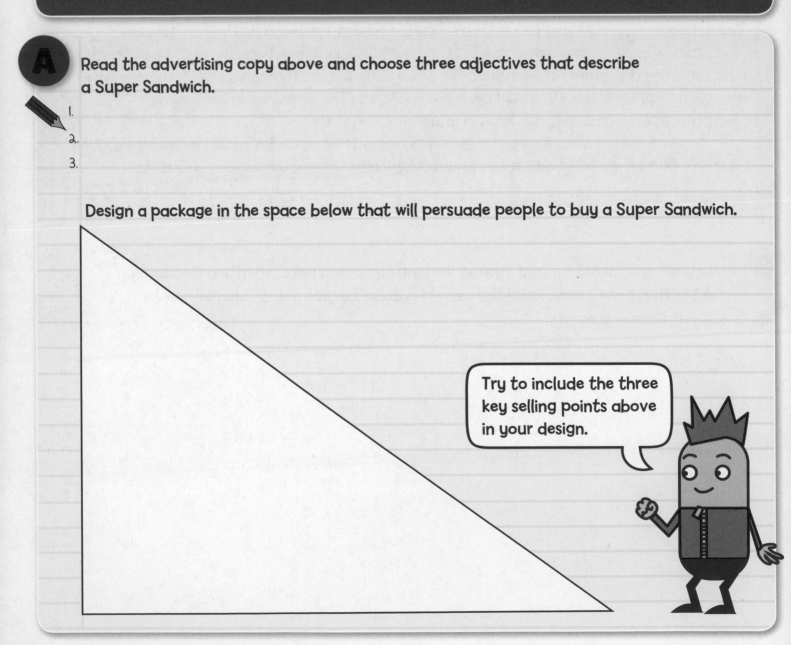

Try to include the three key selling points above in your design.

DEFINITION

persuade: When you cause or convince someone to do something.

B

Write some advertising copy for one of these products. Choose from:

- A mobile phone
- A toy robot dog
- A computer game

Key selling points:

1.

2.

3.

Now design the packaging for your product in the space below.

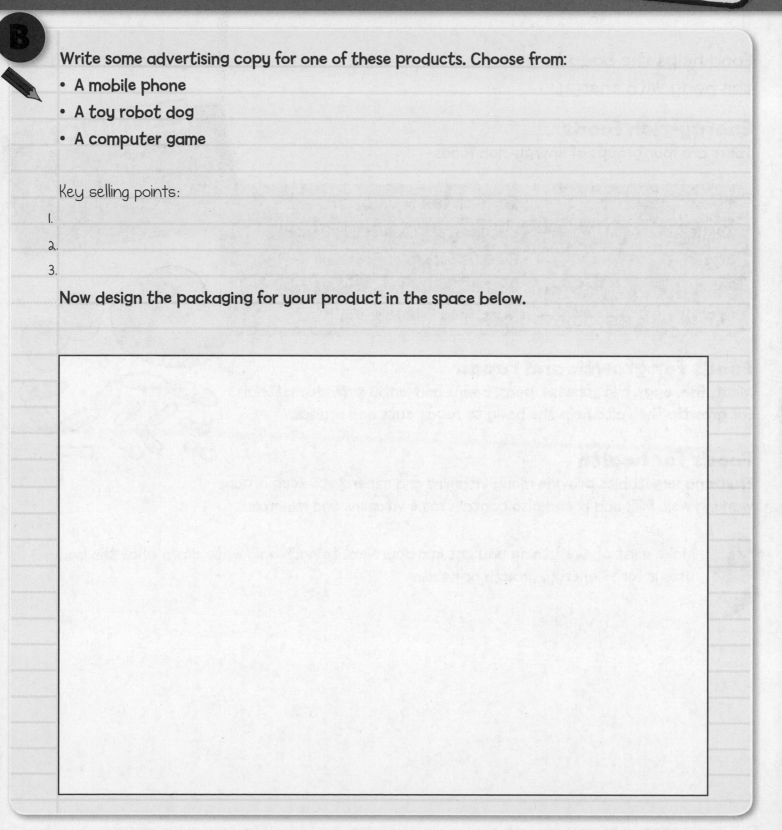

Food and the body

Food helps the body to grow and keeps organs working healthily. It also provides the body with energy.

Energy-rich foods

There are four groups of energy-rich foods.

Food type		Examples
Sugar	⟶	Biscuits, cakes, sweets, fizzy drinks
Starch	⟶	Bread, pasta, potatoes, rice
Fats	⟶	Butter, cheese, milk, sausages
Oils	⟶	Nuts, fried food, oily fish

DEFINITION

organ: A part of the body that performs a particular task in keeping the body alive.

Foods for growth and repair

Meat, fish, eggs, milk, cheese, peas, beans and lentils provide materials for growth. They also help the body to repair cuts and bruises.

Foods for health

Fruit and vegetables provide many vitamins and minerals to keep organs working well. Milk and bread also contain some vitamins and minerals.

A Make a list of everything you eat in a day. Next to each one, write down what the body uses it for — energy, growth or health.

Diet and health

Learning objective: to understand that diets can affect health

A healthy diet contains a wide range of foods to provide the body with everything it needs.

The body and energy

- The body uses most of the energy in food for moving, but it also stores some as fat to keep the body warm.
- If a diet contains more energy than the body needs, the body stores this extra energy as fat.
- Too much fat can make the body unhealthy.

Making changes

- It is easy to change the amount of energy in a diet by changing foods.
- Sugary snacks like cakes can be swapped for fruit, celery, tomatoes or raw carrot.
- Fizzy drinks can be replaced with semi-skimmed milk, which also provides vitamins and minerals for healthy teeth and bones.

B Look at the list that you made in the last activity. Does it contain a large amount of energy-rich foods? Make a list of some healthier options.

The heart and the pulse

Learning objective: to learn that the actions of the heart and pulse are related

The heart pumps the blood around the body. At certain places in the body its beating may be felt as a pulse.

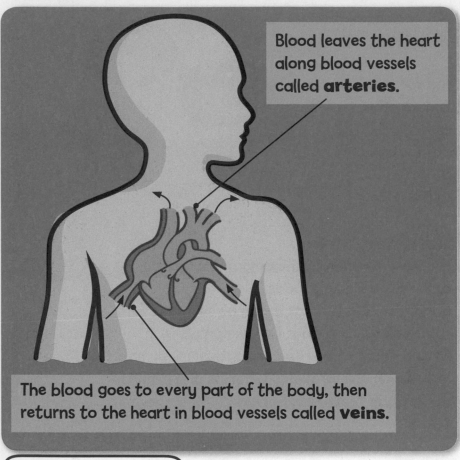

Blood leaves the heart along blood vessels called **arteries**.

The blood goes to every part of the body, then returns to the heart in blood vessels called **veins**.

The pulse
- Find the pulse in your wrist.
- Place the first two fingers of your left hand on the inside of your right wrist.
- Press to find the pulse.

The heart and blood
- The heart is a bag of muscle about the size of a fist.
- The muscles squeeze and relax to make the heart beat.
- This pumps blood around the body.

DEFINITION

blood vessels:
Tubes that carry blood around the body.

Try finding your pulse using the instructions on this page.

A

Fill in the gaps in the paragraph from the word list below.

blood   parts   arteries   vessels   veins   pumps

The heart _____ the blood into the _____ and it travels to all _____ of the body. The _____ returns to the heart in blood _____ called _____ .

Exercise and the pulse

Learning objective: to measure the pulse rate and relate it to exercise

The blood carries food and oxygen round the body. When we exercise, our muscles work harder. They need more food and oxygen, so the heart beats faster.

Measuring the pulse rate

- Measure how fast the heart beats by counting how many times the pulse throbs in a minute. This is called the pulse rate.
- A stopwatch or watch with a second hand can be used as a timer.

How the pulse rate changes

- Sit down and measure your pulse for a minute. This is its resting rate.
- Walk around for two minutes then take it again. See how your pulse changes with exercise.
- Take the pulse every other minute for a while. The pulse should go back to its resting rate.

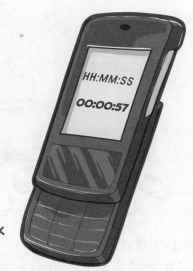

HH:MM:SS
00:00:57

B Draw lines to match the pulse rate with the activity.

65   person running

70   person lying down

90   person standing

120   person walking

Phew! What happens to your pulse when you exercise?

C

Measure your pulse rate when sitting.

Write it here: _____

Measure your pulse rate after walking for two minutes.

Write it here: _____

Predict how your pulse may change after running for two minutes.

Write your prediction here: _____

Measure your pulse rate after running for two minutes.

Write it here: _____

Drugs

Learning objective: to understand that drugs can be helpful or harmful

Certain types of drugs can help the body to recover from illness or injury, but others can make people very unwell.

Helpful drugs
- When someone is ill they may take a medicine to get better.
- Most medicines contain substances called drugs. The drugs may ease pain or help the body to heal or fight infection.

> If a child needs medication, an adult should always be in charge!

Harmful drugs
- Harmful drugs such as ecstasy, cocaine and heroin damage the brain and heart.
- Someone who regularly takes harmful drugs is an addict.
- Some harmful drugs are taken as tablets, but others are smoked or injected into the body.
- Drug addicts may share needles, which spreads deadly diseases.

A

Fill in the gaps in the paragraph from the word list below. (You can use a word more than once!)

drugs	ill	cocaine	killed	medicines

People who are _____ take _____ to get better.
The _____ can contain _____ to help them recover.
Harmful _____ like _____ make people become
addicts. Addicts are in danger of being _____ by the
_____ they take.

DEFINITION

medication: Regular amounts of a medicine (liquid or tablets) taken to treat an illness.

addict: A person who feels they cannot survive without taking a certain drug.

Tobacco and alcohol

Learning objective: to know that tobacco and alcohol are dangerous

Smoking tobacco and drinking alcohol can be extremely harmful.

Tobacco

- Tobacco is smoked in cigarettes, cigars and pipes.
- It contains an addictive drug called nicotine.
- Tobacco smoke damages the lungs.
- It also contains substances that damage the heart and can cause cancers to develop in the throat and lungs.

Alcohol

- Alcohol is found in drinks such as alcopops, beer, cider and wine.
- It affects the brain and the way people think and move.
- Alcohol is processed by the liver. If large amounts of alcohol are drunk regularly the liver may become fatally damaged.
- People who become addicted to alcohol are called alcoholics.

B

Design a poster to discourage people from smoking or drinking too much alcohol.

DEFINITION

liver: A body organ that performs many tasks to keep the body alive.

123

Parts of a flower

Learning objective: to recognize the different parts of a flower

A flower has many parts. The parts work together to help the plant reproduce.

Part of flower	Physical clue	Purpose
Stamen	Has a swollen end	Makes pollen
Petal	Is large and brightly coloured	Attracts insects
Stigma	Has a sticky surface	Receives pollen grains
Ovary	Is at the base of the flower	Grows into fruit, contains ovules
Carpels	Is at the centre of the flower	Has a stigma, style and ovary
Style	Is beneath the stigma	Connects stigma to ovary
Sepal	Is green and bends back	Protects the flower as a bud

A   Use the information in the table to fill in the missing labels on the diagram.

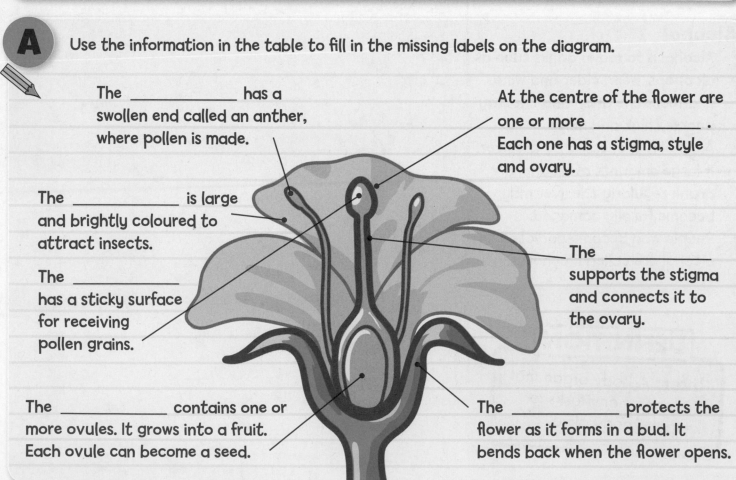

The _____ has a swollen end called an anther, where pollen is made.

The _____ is large and brightly coloured to attract insects.

The _____ has a sticky surface for receiving pollen grains.

The _____ contains one or more ovules. It grows into a fruit. Each ovule can become a seed.

At the centre of the flower are one or more _____ . Each one has a stigma, style and ovary.

The _____ supports the stigma and connects it to the ovary.

The _____ protects the flower as it forms in a bud. It bends back when the flower opens.

124

Pollination

Learning objective: to distinguish between insect and wind pollination

Pollination is the movement of pollen from the stamen of one flower to the stigma of another flower of the same kind. Pollen may be carried by insects or the wind.

Insect pollination

- Insect-pollinated plants have flowers with large, bright petals and a strong scent. These flowers make nectar, on which the insects feed.
- The plants make small amounts of large spiky pollen, which sticks to the insect's body as it brushes past the stamens.
- The pollen is collected by the sticky stigma of the next flower the insect visits.

Wind pollination

- The flowers of wind-pollinated plants do not have large petals, scent or nectar. They have stamens that hang out of the flower and release a large amount of small, smooth pollen grains.
- This is trapped by the feathery stigmas of other wind-pollinated flowers, which hang out like a net to catch pollen as it is blown by.
- All grasses have wind-pollinated flowers.

B Tick or cross these boxes - read back through the text on this page for clues.

> Try to identify the different parts of flowers in your garden or local park.

	Insect-pollinated flower	Wind-pollinated flower
Large petals		
Strong scent		
Nectar		
Little pollen		
Lots of pollen		
Smooth pollen		
Spiky pollen		

Forming fruits

Learning objective: to understand that fruits form after fertilization

A fruit forms from the ovary of a flower after fertilization.

Fertilization

- After a pollen grain sticks to the stigma it enters the ovary.
- Substances in the pollen grain join with other substances in the ovule.

After fertilization

- The ovule grows into a seed.
- The ovary changes into a fruit around the seed.
- Other parts of the flower, such as the petals and stamens, fall away. The sepals may stay in place.

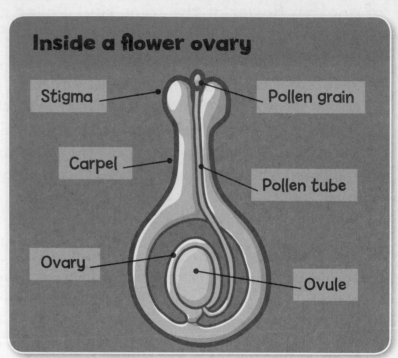

Inside a flower ovary

Stigma — Pollen grain

Carpel — Pollen tube

Ovary — Ovule

Look at the seeds in an apple or tomato. Notice how they are spread out.

A

Match the plant structures on the left with the description of what they do. The first one has been done for you.

Stigma	Turns into a seed after fertilization.
Pollen grain	Makes pollen grains stick.
Pollen tube	Carries a substance from a flower for fertilization.
Ovule	Carries a substance from a pollen grain to an ovule.

DEFINITION

fertilization: The process in which a male cell joins with a female cell and makes a new living thing.

Fruit and seed dispersal

Learning objective: to know that fruits and seeds can be dispersed in different ways

The spreading out of seeds from the parent plant is called dispersal. This gives the seeds plenty of space to grow when they germinate.

Dispersal by the wind
Maple and ash trees have winged fruits. As the fruits fall the wind catches the wings and makes them spin away. The dandelion fruit has a 'parachute', which catches the wind.

Dandelion fruit

Blackberries

Dispersal by animals
Goose grass has fruits covered in hooks, which cling to the fur of passing animals. Succulent berries are eaten by animals, but the seeds pass through their bodies unharmed.

Explosive fruits
When some fruits, such as balsam and lupin, dry they shrink, split open quickly and fling their seeds away.

Lupin pod
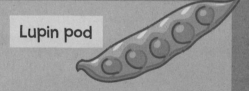

B These phrases summarize the main stages in the life cycle of a plant. Put them in the correct order by writing a number (1 to 6) in each box.

- ☐ Plant fully grown.
- ☐ Seedling starts to grow.
- ☐ Plant makes flowers.
- ☐ Seed germinates.
- ☐ Plant disperses fruit.
- ☐ Flowers make fruits.

DEFINITION

germinate: When the tiny plant inside a seed bursts out and starts to grow into a seedling.

succulent: Soft and juicy.

life cycle: The stages in the life of a living thing.

127

The human life cycle

Learning objective: to know about the different stages in the human life cycle

From the moment you are born you are growing and changing. In later life you stop growing, but you never stop changing.

The human life cycle is divided into stages.

Baby
- Cannot do anything for itself.
- Sleeps a lot of the time.
- Feeds on milk.
- Learns to sit up at about six months.

Toddler
- Learns to stand and walk at about one year old.
- Eats a range of foods.
- Begins to learn to talk.

Adult
- Eventually stops growing.
- Hair may begin to turn grey.
- Skin may become wrinkly.

Child
- More skilled at walking and talking.
- Continues to grow.
- Learns many new skills.

Adolescent
- At about 11 or 12 years, girls begin to change into women.
- At about 11 or 12 years, boys begin to change into men.
- Process takes about three years and is known as adolescence.

How do you think you will change in the future?

A Look at photos of yourself as a baby and compare them with how you look now. What are the differences?

Then	Now

Animal life cycles

Learning objective: to compare the life cycles of different animals

Many animals have life cycles where the young look like smaller versions of the adults. But in some animals the young are completely different from the adults.

Insects

- Most baby insects start life as larvae or caterpillars, then change into pupae.
- Eventually they change to become adults.
- This is called metamorphosis.

The **caterpillar** hatches.

It then changes into a **pupa**.

The butterfly lays its **eggs** on a leaf.

The **butterfly** emerges.

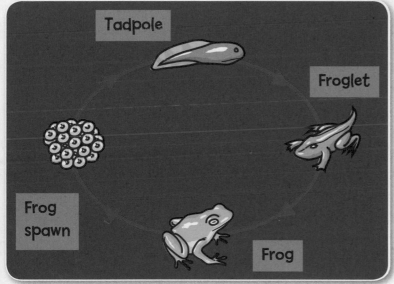

Tadpole

Froglet

Frog spawn

Frog

Amphibians

- Frogs and toads start life as tadpoles.
- As they grow they develop legs, their tails disappear and their head shape changes.

Life cycles and extinction

- A life cycle is completed when the adult animal has young. They carry on living after their parents die.
- If an animal species is rare, it may never find a mate. The species may die out, or become extinct.

DEFINITION

species: A type of living thing. All individuals of the species have very similar features. The males and females can breed to produce young.

B Put these words in the correct places below.

disappears   jelly   hatches   tail   legs   egg

A frog's _____ is surrounded by _____ .

A tadpole _____ from the egg. It has a long _____

and looks like a little fish. In time the tadpole grows _____

and a big head and its tail _____ . When this happens it

has turned into a frog.

The air we breathe

Learning objective: to learn that air is a real material

The air in a room can't be seen or felt, but when you stand in a wind you can feel it and see its effects. Air is a real substance. It is a mixture of gases.

Air has weight

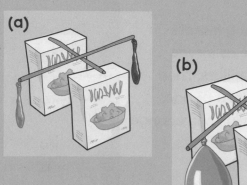

(a)

(b)

- Two empty balloons are tied to either end of a stick.
- The stick is rested across two boxes so the two ends balance.
- One balloon is inflated and placed back on the stick.
- The stick no longer balances in the centre because the inflated balloon is heavier.
- This shows that air has weight.

Water fills the gaps

Water pools on the surface when the gaps are full

Air fills the gaps

Pouring water into soil pushes the air out of the gaps between the soil particles. If you measure how much water you can pour into a dish of soil before the water starts to pool at the surface, you can tell how much air was in the soil.

A These pictures show how much water was in a measuring cylinder before and after it was poured onto soil to fill the gaps.

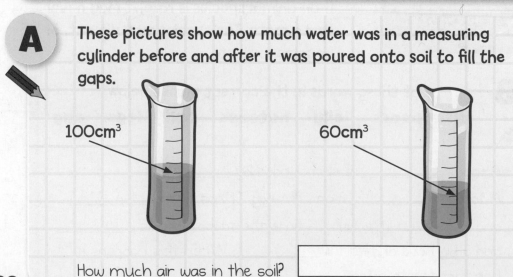

100cm³

60cm³

How much air was in the soil?

DEFINITION

gas: A substance with no fixed shape, which flows in all directions and can be compressed, or squashed.

Gases

Learning objective: to understand that there are many different gases

There are many different gases, and each one has its own properties and uses. The main gases in air are nitrogen, oxygen, carbon dioxide and water vapour.

GAS	PROPERTIES
Oxygen	Oxygen helps us release energy from our food. It lets things burn in it.
Carbon dioxide	We produce carbon dioxide as we release energy from food and breathe it out. Plants use carbon dioxide from the air to make food. Carbon dioxide is squashed into drinks to make them fizzy.
Helium	Helium is the gas used in party balloons. It makes the balloon rise because helium is lighter than air.
Natural gas	This gas is called methane and is made from the decomposing bodies of huge numbers of tiny sea creatures that lived long ago and became covered in rock. Methane is used in gas cookers and fires.

B

Match the gases on the left with the description of their property or use. The first one has been done for you.

Oxygen   Used in some cookers.

Helium   Used to make food by plants.

Natural gas   Lighter than air.

Carbon dioxide   Lets things burn in it.

DEFINITION

decomposing: The rotting down of the bodies of dead animals or plants into simple substances such as minerals and gases.

131

Melting

Learning objective: to understand that solids can change into liquids by melting

A solid has a fixed shape, but when it reaches melting point it turns into a liquid. The temperature at which a substance melts is measured in degrees Celsius (°C).

Examples of melting

Chocolate can melt in a warm pocket.

Butter melts when it is put on hot food, such as boiled potatoes or toast.

The wax around the wick of a burning candle melts and forms a pool.

An ice cube melts in a glass.

Inside the Earth there are places where it is so hot that the rock melts. (The molten rock bursts through the Earth's surface at the vent of a volcano.)

The melting process

As the temperature of a solid rises close to its melting point, it starts to soften and its shape starts to sag and flatten. At the melting point, the substance flows away.

Reversible change

Melting is a reversible change because, if the liquid substance is cooled down again, it changes back into a solid.

> What do you think would happen to the melted chocolate if you put it in the fridge to cool down?

Use these words to fill in the spaces in the paragraph below. You can use the words more than once if you need to.

point   temperature   chocolate   shape
liquid   warmer

A piece of _____ was left on a sunny windowsill. As it got _____ its firm sides started to sag and it began to lose its _____. When the _____ reached melting _____ the chocolate turned into a _____ and dripped off the windowsill.

Freezing

A liquid can change into a solid by a process called freezing. The temperature at which this happens is called the freezing point.

Freezing water
Water freezes at a temperature of 0°C and becomes a solid we call ice. The ice has a fixed shape, which it keeps until it starts to melt again.

Moulding metal
Metals have to be heated very strongly to make them melt. When solid metal is turned into a liquid it can be poured into a mould. As the metal cools, it freezes and becomes a solid again. The solid will have the same shape as the mould the liquid was poured into.

Reversible change
Freezing is a reversible change. If a solid substance is heated up again it changes back into a liquid.

B

Substance	Freezing point (°C)	
Beeswax	64°C	☐
Water	0°C	☐
Chocolate	25°C	☐
Lard	43°C	☐
Pewter	240°C	☐

A substance's freezing point is the same as its melting point.

This table shows the freezing points of five substances. In which order do they freeze as the temperature drops from 250°C to 0°C?

Write the order from 1 to 5 in the boxes on the right of the table.

☐

How many would freeze if the temperature fell to just 30°C?

133

From liquid to gas

Learning objective: to know that liquids change to gases by evaporation or boiling

Liquids can change into gases in two ways - by evaporating or boiling.

Evaporation

- Water is placed in a saucer.
- The water at the surface in contact with the air changes into a gas called water vapour.
- This process of change is called evaporation.
- The water vapour spreads out in the air.

Conditions for evaporation

- Evaporation takes place at normal air temperature.
- It speeds up if the air is warmer or moving fast.
- Evaporation also speeds up if the air is dry and does not contain much water vapour.

3. Water vapour spreads out in the air.

2. Water turns into water vapour.

1. Water at the surface is in contact with the air.

Boiling

- Water boils at 100°C.
- A gas called steam forms inside the liquid and makes bubbles.
- The bubbles rise to the top and pop into the air.

Evaporation and boiling are reversible changes. Can you explain why this is?

A This table shows the results of an experiment into speed of evaporation in different conditions.

Condition	Time to evaporate (hours)
Cold	10
Hot	2
Still	9
Windy	3
Moist air	12
Dry air	3

What are the best conditions for evaporation to take place quickly?

From gas to liquid

Learning objective: to know that gases turn to liquids by condensation

Gases can change back into liquids when they cool down in a process called condensation. We also use the word condensation to describe the water that forms on the inside of windows in warm kitchens and bathrooms.

Water vapour and steam
- As water vapour rises it cools down and condenses on dust particles floating in the air.
- This makes the white clouds we call steam.
- You cannot see steam in bubbles.
- You cannot see steam when it enters very hot air.

Breathing out
- There is water vapour in our breath. On a cold day we can see it condense in the air and look like the steam above a kettle.
- If you breathe out onto a cold drink can from a fridge you will see water droplets form on the can as the vapour in your breath condenses.

Steam cools and condenses to form a cloud of water droplets.

Steam cannot be seen as it rushes out of a kettle spout.

Condensation is a reversible change. Can you explain why?

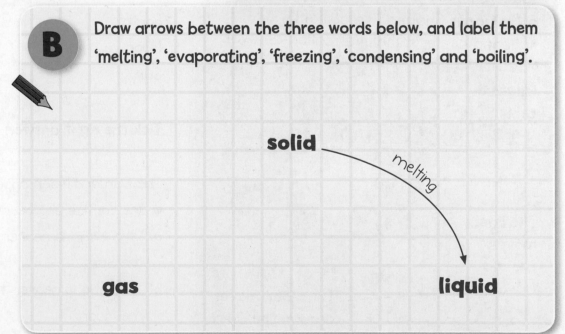

B Draw arrows between the three words below, and label them 'melting', 'evaporating', 'freezing', 'condensing' and 'boiling'.

solid

melting

gas

liquid

The Sun, Earth and Moon

Learning objective: to compare the Sun, the Earth and the Moon

The Sun, the Earth and the Moon are ball-shaped objects in space.

The Sun

- The Sun is a star. It is made of two gases: hydrogen and helium.
- Inside the Sun, hydrogen is changed into helium.
- This produces light and heat, which spread out through space.

The Earth and the Moon

- The Earth is a planet made of rock and mostly covered in water. It moves anticlockwise around the Sun in an elliptical orbit, once every year.
- The Moon is also made of rock. It moves anticlockwise around the Earth in an almost circular orbit, once every month.
- The Sun is many times larger than the Moon. They appear roughly the same size to us because the Moon is much closer to the Earth.

Never look directly at the Sun - it could damage your eyesight.

DEFINITION

axis: The imaginary line around which the Earth spins.

orbit: The path taken by one object in space as it moves around another.

elliptical: Shaped like a slightly flattened circle, sometimes called an oval.

A

Do some research and find out the diameter of the Sun, the Earth and the Moon. Match them up below by drawing lines between them.

Earth	1,392,000km
Moon	3476km
Sun	12,756km

Tick the right answer:

The Sun and Moon appear the same size in the Earth's sky because...

a) ...the Moon is nearer the Earth than the Sun. ☐

b) ...the Sun is nearer the Earth than the Moon. ☐

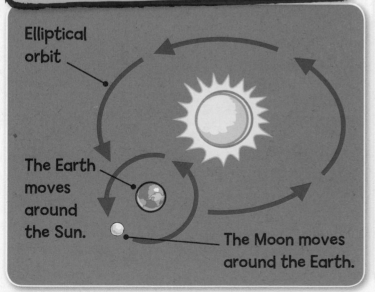

Elliptical orbit

The Earth moves around the Sun.

The Moon moves around the Earth.

The Earth in its orbit

Learning objective: to link the orbit of the Earth with the seasons

The way the Earth tilts in space and makes its journey around the Sun produces long periods of certain kinds of weather that are known as seasons.

The Earth's axis
- The Earth spins on its axis.
- The axis is tilted just over 23 degrees from vertical and keeps pointing in the same direction as the Earth orbits the Sun.

The hemispheres and the seasons
- The equator is an invisible line that runs around the middle of the Earth.
- The half of the Earth above the equator is called the Northern Hemisphere.
- The half below the equator is called the Southern Hemisphere.
- When a hemisphere is angled towards the Sun, it's summer there. When it's pointing away, it is winter.
- Spring and autumn occur when neither hemisphere is pointing towards the Sun.

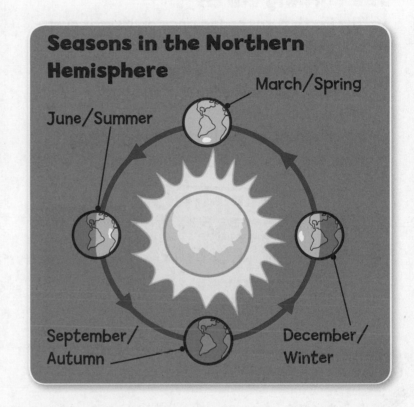

Seasons in the Northern Hemisphere

June/Summer

March/Spring

September/ Autumn

December/ Winter

B

1. What season is it now? Draw the Earth's position round the Sun and label it.

2. Where will the Earth be in six months' time? Make a drawing and add a label.

3. Draw and label where it will be when it is your birthday.

Day and night

Day and night occur due to the turning of the Earth on its axis.

The turning Earth

- The Earth turns round once on its axis every 24 hours. During that time, all parts of the Earth spend some time facing the Sun.
- When a part of the Earth is facing the Sun, it is daytime there.
- When a part of the Earth is facing away from the Sun, it is night-time there.

DEFINITION

clockwise: The direction taken by the hands of a clock.

anticlockwise: The opposite direction to that taken by the hands of a clock.

The Earth from above the North Pole

The Earth turns in an anticlockwise direction on its axis.

A

1. Imagine you were above the North Pole in a space ship. Would the Earth below you seem to be turning clockwise or anticlockwise?

   Look at the places marked A, B and C on this picture of the Earth and the Sun. Read the questions, then write A, B or C in the boxes below.

2. In which place is it midnight? ☐

3. In which place is it midday? ☐

4. In which place is it dawn? ☐

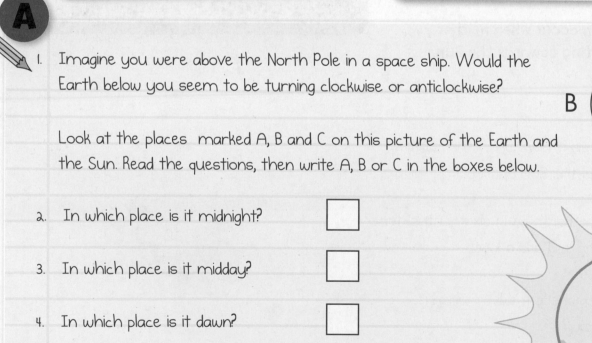

The Sun in the sky

Learning objective: to learn how the Sun changes position in the sky

The Sun appears to move quickly across the sky. This movement is not due to the Sun. The spinning of the Earth makes the Sun appear to move.

The Sun and shadows

* As the Sun moves across the sky, the length and direction of shadows change.

The path of the Sun

Sun rises in the east

Midday

Sun sets in the west

In this diagram, we are facing south, so east is on the left and west is on the right.

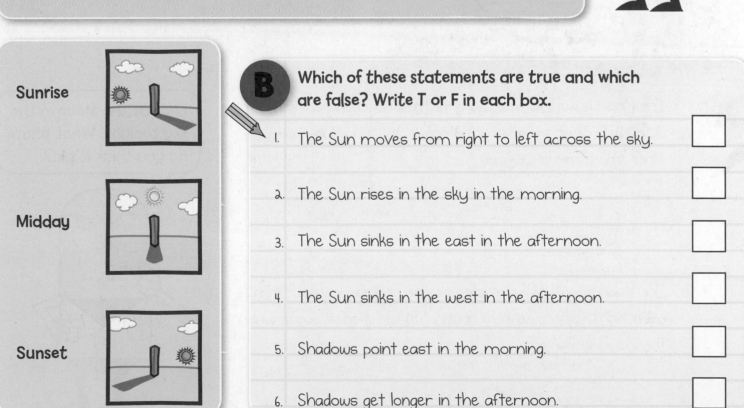

Sunrise

Midday

Sunset

B Which of these statements are true and which are false? Write T or F in each box.

1. The Sun moves from right to left across the sky. ☐

2. The Sun rises in the sky in the morning. ☐

3. The Sun sinks in the east in the afternoon. ☐

4. The Sun sinks in the west in the afternoon. ☐

5. Shadows point east in the morning. ☐

6. Shadows get longer in the afternoon. ☐

The phases of the Moon

Learning objective: to understand how the phases of the Moon change

The sunlit areas of the Moon change as the Moon moves in its orbit.

As the Moon goes around the Earth the Sun shines on half of the Moon. But from the Earth we can sometimes see only part of the sunlit areas. The sunlit areas seen from the Earth are called the phases of the Moon.

The path of the Moon
The half of the Moon and the part of the Earth facing the Sun are lit up by the Sun.

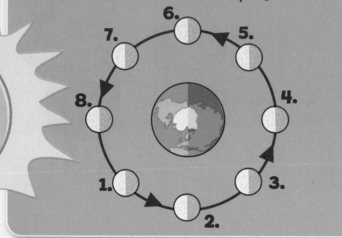

The phases of the Moon
Some of the phases of the Moon as they appear from the Earth.

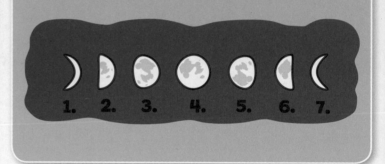

A

1. The Moon is said to be waxing as the phases increase in size each night towards a full moon. Which phases occur when the Moon is waxing?

2. The Moon is said to be waning as the phases decrease in size each night towards a new moon. Which phases occur when the Moon is waning?

Look at the Moon in the sky tonight. What phase do you think it's in?

The Solar System

Learning objective: to know how the Sun, the Moon and the Earth fit into the Solar System

The Solar System formed about 5000 million years ago. It consists of the Sun, the planets (including the Earth) and their moons, asteroids and comets.

Moons

- The Earth has one moon.
- Mars has two moons.
- Neptune has 13 moons.
- Uranus has 27 moons.
- Saturn has 53 moons.
- Jupiter has 63 moons.

Asteroids

- Asteroids form a ring, or belt, between the orbits of Mars and Jupiter.

DEFINITION

asteroid: A piece of rock left over from the time when the Solar System formed that moves in an orbit around the Sun.

The planets
The Sun is at the centre of the Solar System, and the eight planets move around it.

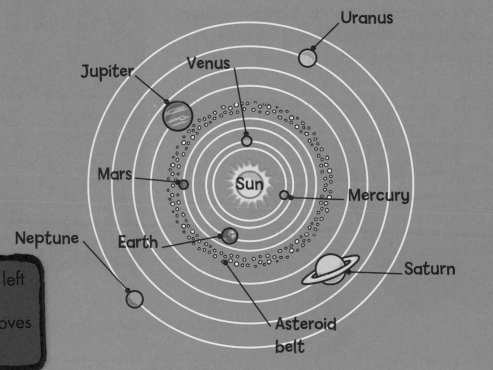

B Imagine you were on a space shuttle beyond Neptune and you travelled to the Sun and back. Write down the planets you would pass on your journey and when you would go through the asteroid belt.

Vibration

Learning objective: to learn that sounds are made by vibrations

A sound is made when something vibrates. A vibration is a to and fro or an up and down movement. Vibrations can move through different materials.

Making vibrations

- If a ruler is held firmly over the edge of a table and 'twanged', it vibrates up and down and makes a sound.
- An elastic band stretched between finger and thumb vibrates to and fro when it is plucked. It also makes a sound.

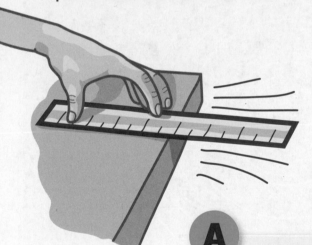

Travelling sound

- When an object vibrates in air, the air around it starts to vibrate.
- This makes air further away vibrate.
- The vibration passes through the air as a wave – a sound wave.

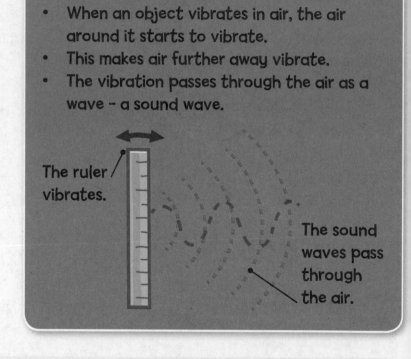

The ruler vibrates.

The sound waves pass through the air.

A

Try twanging a ruler over the edge of a table.

This table shows the speed of sound waves through some materials.

Material	Speed (m per second)
Air	343
Brick	3650
Carbon dioxide	259
Fresh water	1497
Sea water	1531
Wood	4670

Tick the correct box:

Sound travels fastest through...   gases ☐   liquids ☐   solids ☐

Sound travels slowest through...   gases ☐   liquids ☐   solids ☐

Loud and soft

Learning objective: to understand about loud and soft sounds

Large vibrations make loud sounds and small vibrations make quiet sounds. Vibrations may be absorbed into some materials so that little or no sound is heard. These materials are called sound insulators.

Measuring loudness

The decibel (dB) is the unit used to measure the loudness of sounds. Here are some examples of quiet and loud sounds.

Sound	Loudness (dB)
Road drill	110
Vacuum cleaner	80
Busy street	70
People talking	50
Quiet street	40
Whisper	30
Pin drop	10

Guess how loud it is around you now using the decibel scale. Try it at other times too.

Sound insulation

Try testing materials to see how well they insulate sound.

- Wrap the material around a sound source, such as a radio.
- Measure the distance at which the source sound can no longer be heard.

B

1. How do you think a sound insulation test could be made fair?

2. A radio could not be heard 2 metres away when wrapped in material A and could not be heard 50 centimetres away when wrapped in material B. Which material was the better sound insulator?

Pitch

Learning objective: to understand that pitch describes how high or low a note is

A high-pitched sound is one that sounds like 'Ping!' or 'Peep!'
A low-pitched sound is one that sounds like 'Pong!' or 'Boom!'

Pitch and loudness

- Pitch and loudness do not affect each other.
- A high-pitched or low-pitched sound can be made either quietly or loudly.
- Whisper and shout 'Ping!' and 'Pong!' to check.

Vibration, pitch and frequency

- An object that vibrates slowly makes a sound with a low pitch.
- An object that vibrates quickly makes a sound with a high pitch.
- The frequency of a sound is the number of vibrations that pass in a second. Low-pitched sounds have low frequencies and high-pitched sounds have high frequencies.
- The unit for measuring frequency is the hertz (Hz).

A

Here are the frequencies of some common sounds.

> How does the pitch change when you change the length of a vibrating ruler?

Sound	Frequency (Hz)	
Baby's first cry	432	☐
Bottom C note on piano	32	☐
Cat's purr	25	1
Chainsaw	4000	☐
Ordinary voice	250	☐
Thunder	40	☐
Top note on piano	4096	☐

Write the numbers 1 to 7 in the boxes to arrange them in order of pitch, starting with the lowest. The first one has been done for you.

Musical instruments

Learning objective: to learn how pitch can be changed in musical instruments

Each note of a musical instrument is a different pitch from the others. The notes played on an instrument are changed by varying the way in which the instrument vibrates.

Drums
- The pitch can be raised by tightening the skin of the drum.
- Small drums have a higher pitch because the skins are made of less material and vibrate faster when hit.

Stringed instruments
- The pitch depends on thickness, tightness and length of the string.
- A long, thick, loose string has the lowest pitch.
- A short, thin, tight string has the highest pitch.

Wind instruments
- The pitch is due to the length of the vibrating column inside it.
- A long air column makes a low-pitched sound.
- A short column makes a high-pitched sound.

Percussion instruments
Percussion instruments are struck to produce a sound. These include drums, cymbals and gongs.

Stringed instruments
These instruments are strummed or stroked with a bow. They include guitars, violins, cellos and banjoes.

Wind instruments
Wind instruments are blown into. They include woodwind (e.g. clarinet, flute) and brass (e.g. trumpet).

1. Which drum has the lower pitch? Drum A, which has a diameter of 10cm, or drum B, which is 20cm across?

2. Which string has the higher pitch? String A, which is long, thick and loose, or string B, which is short, thin and tight?

3. Closing holes on a recorder makes the air column longer. Does this make the pitch higher or lower?

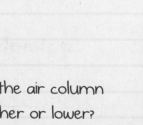

The growing plant

Learning objective: to learn that a plant needs light, air and water to grow well

Plants make their own food using energy from the Sun and materials from the air and soil. The food is used for growth and making flowers, fruits and seeds.

Collecting ingredients
- Roots soak up water from the soil.
- Leaves draw water up the plant.
- Leaves are covered with tiny holes that let water vapour escape.
- As water escapes into the air, more water is sucked up through the roots.
- Carbon dioxide also passes in through the holes.

Making food
- Light shines on the leaf.
- This provides energy for the water and carbon dioxide in the leaf to change into food.
- This process is called photosynthesis.
- Oxygen is also made in this process. It passes out of the leaf through the holes.

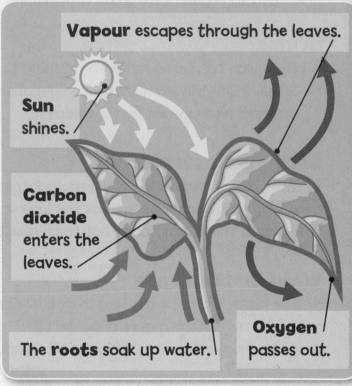

Vapour escapes through the leaves.

Sun shines.

Carbon dioxide enters the leaves.

The **roots** soak up water.

Oxygen passes out.

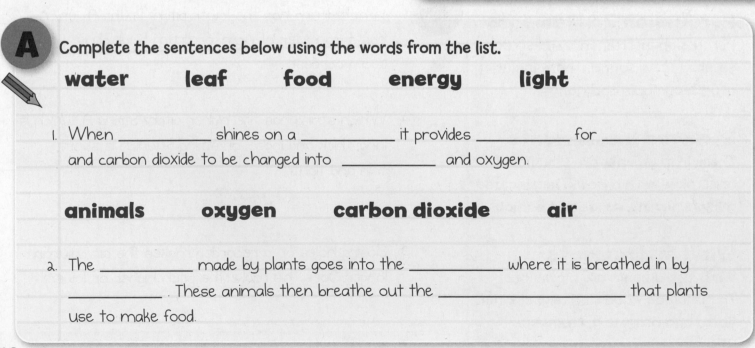

A Complete the sentences below using the words from the list.

water   **leaf**   **food**   **energy**   **light**

1. When _____ shines on a _____ it provides _____ for _____ and carbon dioxide to be changed into _____ and oxygen.

animals   **oxygen**   **carbon dioxide**   **air**

2. The _____ made by plants goes into the _____ where it is breathed in by _____ . These animals then breathe out the _____ that plants use to make food.

Roots and soil

DEFINITION

humus: The remains of dead plants and animals held in the soil.

Learning objective: to learn that plants take water and minerals from the soil

The roots hold the plant in the soil. They take up minerals from the soil that are dissolved in the water.

Types of root
There are two main types of root – tap roots and fibrous roots.

Tap roots
A tap root is a long, thick root, which stores food and grows deep into the soil. A carrot has a tap root.

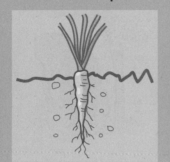

Fibrous roots
Fibrous roots are long, thin and branching and spread out in the soil around the plant. Grass has fibrous roots.

The parts of the soil
* The soil is made from rocky particles. The largest particles are pieces of gravel.
* Sand grains are smaller, silt is smaller still and clay particles are the smallest.
* All these particles are bound together by humus. The rocky particles and the humus contain minerals that dissolve in water.

Minerals and plant growth
* All plants need some minerals to grow healthily.
* Some farmers and gardeners use fertilizer, which has extra minerals to help plants grow healthily.

B

1. How is a tap root different from a fibrous root?

Soil with lots of large rocky particles drains well, but soil with small rocky particles drains poorly.
Here are three soils:

A = gravelly soil   **B = sandy soil**   **C = clay soil**

2. Which soil drains best? ☐
   Which has the worst drainage? ☐

Plant and animal habitats

Learning objective: to learn how plants and animals rely on each other for survival

Many animals feed on plants, but all animals need plants in some way to help them to survive. Plants depend on animals for survival too.

Why animals need plants

Plants provide food, habitats and shelter for animals.

Beetle hides in tree bark.

Spider spins web on twigs.

Deer eats grass and shelters under tree.

Bird uses plants to build nests.

Why plants need animals

Bees help plants to spread pollen. Some animals spread fruits and seeds that stick to their fur or feathers, and many animals eat fruits and spread the seeds in their droppings.

Animal droppings also provide the soil with minerals for plant growth.

A

Look at the pictures above and answer these questions.

1. Which animals are using plants for shelter?

2. Which animal is using a plant as food?

3. Which animal is using a plant to help it set a trap?

148

Understanding keys

Learning objective: to learn how to use a key to identify animal species

A key is a number of features about organisms set out as questions. As each question is answered you move on to the next one until you identify the organism.

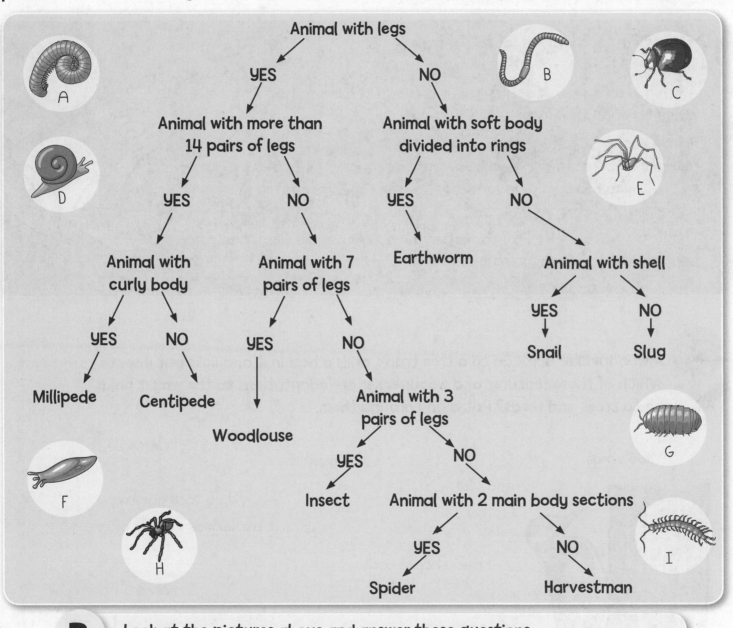

Animal with legs

YES → Animal with more than 14 pairs of legs

NO → Animal with soft body divided into rings

Animal with more than 14 pairs of legs
YES → Animal with curly body
NO → Animal with 7 pairs of legs

Animal with curly body
YES → Millipede
NO → Centipede

Animal with 7 pairs of legs
YES → Woodlouse
NO → Animal with 3 pairs of legs

Animal with 3 pairs of legs
YES → Insect
NO → Animal with 2 main body sections

Animal with 2 main body sections
YES → Spider
NO → Harvestman

Animal with soft body divided into rings
YES → Earthworm
NO → Animal with shell

Animal with shell
YES → Snail
NO → Slug

B Look at the pictures above and answer these questions.
Identify the animals labelled A to I using the key.

A _____   B _____   C _____

D _____   E _____   F _____

G _____   H _____   I _____

Adaptation

Learning objective: to know that living things adapt to survive in their habitats

Living things have body features that help them to survive in a certain habitat. These special features are called adaptations.

Adapting to a pond habitat

- A fish has overlapping scales and is covered in slime to help it move easily through the water as it swims.

- A frog has webbed feet to push on the water and powerful leg muscles to help it swim quickly. Its eyes are on top of its head so that it can lie safely underwater and pop its eyes above the surface to look for predators.

- The heron has long legs for wading in deep water and a long, sharp beak that is adapted for stabbing frogs and fish.

A A woodpecker holds on to a tree trunk, drills a hole in it and licks out insects. Which of these features of a woodpecker are adaptations to the way it holds on to trees and feeds? Put a ring around them.

two wings   two eyes   lays eggs

stiff tail
feathers   two toes pointing
                                     backwards instead of one

chisel-shaped beak
                                            makes a harsh call

                        strong claws
strong skull

                                        feathery crest
            long tongue   on head

Food chains

Learning objective: to learn that living things in a habitat are linked by food chains

Food passes through a habitat along links called food chains.

Link 1
Any part of a plant, such as a seed or leaves, may start a food chain.

Link 2
A plant-eating animal, such as a snail, beetle, rabbit or deer. It is a herbivore, or primary consumer.

Link 3
An animal that eats other animals, such as a spider, frog or shrew. It is a carnivore, or secondary consumer.

Link 4
A large carnivore, such as a fox, owl or heron, which eats smaller carnivores. It is a tertiary consumer.

Prey and predator

An animal that is eaten by another animal is called the prey. The animal that eats the prey is called a predator. A predator is always a carnivore, but prey can be either herbivores or carnivores.

A simple food chain

Lettuce leaf   Slug   Frog   Heron

DEFINITION

herbivore: An animal that feeds on plants.

carnivore: An animal that feeds on other animals.

B Make a food chain using these organisms:

beetle   **seed**   **owl**   **shrew**

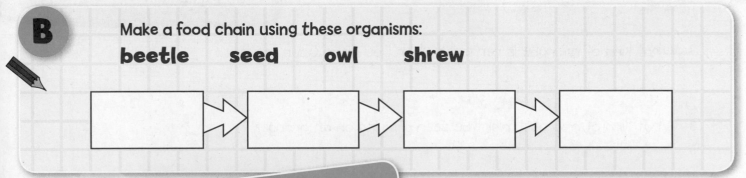

Remember!
In a food chain, the arrow goes from the food to the feeder.

Micro-organisms

Learning objective: to understand that micro-organisms are tiny living things

Micro-organisms are also called microbes. There are three different kinds of micro-organism – viruses, bacteria and some types of fungi.

Viruses

- Viruses cause diseases such as colds, influenza, chicken pox, measles and rabies.

> Achoo! A cold cannot be cured with antibiotics because it is a virus.

Bacteria

- Many bacteria feed on the remains of dead plants and animals and on animal waste.
- They recycle the materials from which living things are made.
- Some bacteria cause diseases like cholera, typhoid and food poisoning.

Fungi

- Moulds and yeast are fungi.
- Moulds spread in the air as tiny particles called spores. When a spore lands on a suitable surface it grows threads and makes a fuzzy patch.
- Moulds are important in recycling materials for living things.
- Moulds can also make good food turn bad.

DEFINITION

fungi: A plant-like organism that does not make its own food but feeds on other materials made by plants and animals.

A

1. What kind of microbe might give you a cold?

2. What kind of microbe is removed when you clean your teeth?

3. What kind of microbe might be seen growing on an orange?

4. What kind of microbe makes the contents of a compost bin rot?

Living with microbes

Learning objective: to understand that microbes can be either harmful or useful

Microbes live in the air, in water and on all kinds of surfaces. We can fight or control the harmful ones and use some others to make food.

Preventing and fighting disease

Stop microbes spreading	If you have a cold, cough or sneeze into a handkerchief. Always wash your hands before eating. Keep rubbish covered to stop flies getting to it.
Keep clean	Make sure the kitchen, cutlery and crockery are clean. Clean your teeth at least twice a day.
Vaccination	Vaccinate against serious diseases.
Medicines	Some infections caused by harmful bacteria can be cured by taking medicines called antibiotics.

Microbes in food

- Certain kinds of harmless bacteria are added to warm milk to make cheese and yoghurt. Harmless moulds may also be added to some cheeses to make them 'blue' and add extra flavour.
- Yeast is a microbe that is mixed with flour, sugar and water to make dough. The yeast microbes feed on sugar and produce bubbles in the dough, which gives bread its spongy texture and makes it rise.

B

What would happen if a bread-making mixture contained only water, flour and yeast? Fill in the gaps using words from this list.

firm   **bubbles**   **sugar**   **spongy**

The bread would not have _____ in it and its texture would be _____ , not _____ . This is because the yeast needs _____ to feed on to make the bread rise.

Dissolving and filtering

Learning objective: to learn that some solutions cannot be separated by filtering

When some substances are mixed with water, they dissolve in it. Other substances do not dissolve, and they can be separated from the water by filtering.

Dissolving

- When a solid dissolves, it breaks up into tiny particles.
- The dissolved mixture is called a solution.
- A coloured solid, such as coffee granules, spreads its colour through the water.

Filtering

- A filter can trap solid particles that have not dissolved.
- The liquid passes through the holes in the filter.
- The solid particles remain behind.
- A filter cannot separate a dissolved solid from a solution.

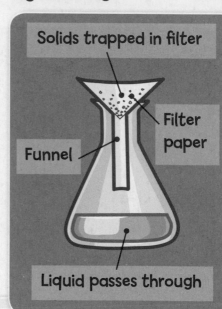

Solids trapped in filter

Filter paper

Funnel

Liquid passes through

A   This table shows the results of an experiment in which different substances were added to water.

Substance	Dissolved
Sand	No
Sugar	Yes
Bath salts	Yes
Flour	No
Custard powder	No
Table salt	Yes

1. Which substances can be separated from the water by filtering?

2. Look at the picture above. Can you describe how a filter works?

Recovering dissolved solids

Learning objective: to learn what happens when water in a solution is changed to gas

Water is changed into a gas by evaporation and by boiling. If the water contains dissolved solids, they remain behind because they do not change into a gas.

Separation
- If a solution is left to evaporate, the dissolved solids will remain behind in the bottom of the container.
- If a solution is boiled for long enough, all of the water will change to steam, and the solid that was dissolved is left behind.

The liquid evaporates   Solids are left behind

Steam condenses on cool surface

Steam rises from the boiling water

Condensation
- If a cold surface is held over boiling water, the steam hits it and cools quickly.
- It condenses and forms a liquid – water.
- If the steam came from a solution, the condensed water will be pure because none of the dissolved solid will be present.

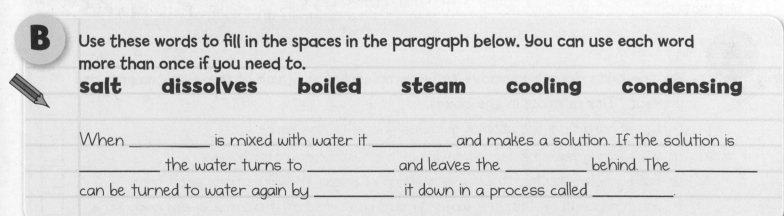

B Use these words to fill in the spaces in the paragraph below. You can use each word more than once if you need to.

salt   dissolves   boiled   steam   cooling   condensing

When _____ is mixed with water it _____ and makes a solution. If the solution is _____ the water turns to _____ and leaves the _____ behind. The _____ can be turned to water again by _____ it down in a process called _____.

The speed of dissolving

The speed of dissolving is affected by the amount of stirring, the temperature of the water and the size of the particles entering the water.

When a solid dissolves

- A solid breaks up into tiny particles when it dissolves.
- The solid particles fill gaps between the water particles.

Stirring, size and temperature

- Investigate the effect of stirring by adding the solid to the water without stirring. Time how long it takes to dissolve.
- Repeat the experiment, stirring the mixture slowly. Then do it again, stirring more quickly. Compare the results.
- Particle size affects how long a solid takes to dissolve. Compare caster sugar (small particles), with granulated sugar (medium-sized particles), then a sugar lump (large particle).
- The temperature of the liquid also affects how a solid dissolves. Repeat the experiment using cold, warm, then hot water.

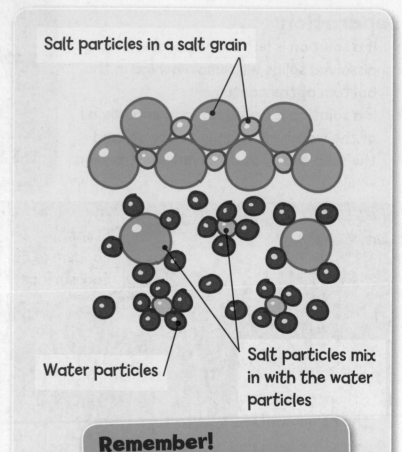

Salt particles in a salt grain

Water particles

Salt particles mix in with the water particles

Remember!
For a test on the speed of dissolving to be fair, the same amount of solid and liquid must be used throughout.

A

For the tests described above to be completely fair, which of these statements are correct? Tick or cross in the boxes.

1. In the stirring test the size of particles should be the same size. ☐
2. In the stirring test the temperature of the water should be the same. ☐
3. In the particle size test the same volume of sugar should be used each time. ☐
4. In the temperature test the water should be stirred at the same speed each time. ☐

Charts and graphs

Learning objective: to learn how and when to use a bar chart and a line graph

Some data is best displayed as a bar chart, while other data is best displayed by a line graph.

Using a bar chart

A bar chart is best when the data has a few definite values, such as sugar particle size.

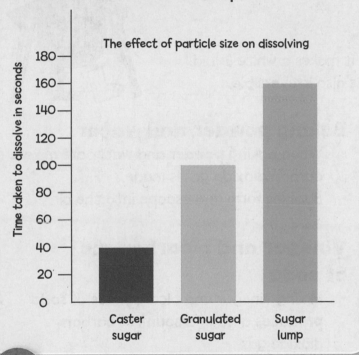

Using a line graph

A line graph is best when the data have a wide range of values, such as temperature.

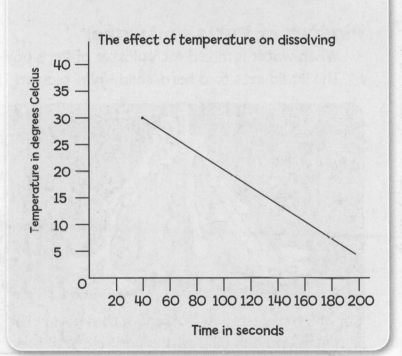

B

Look at the graphs above and answer these questions.

DEFINITION

data: Information, often in the form of measurements, that is obtained from experiments.

1. How long does it take for the caster sugar to dissolve?

2. How long does it take for the solid to dissolve at 30 degrees Celsius?

3. What is the water temperature when a solid takes 100 seconds to dissolve?

Irreversible changes

Learning objective: to know that some changes to materials cannot be reversed

Some changes are irreversible. This means that the materials that took part in a process cannot be recovered easily.

Flour and water

- When flour is added to water it makes a sticky dough.
- The water cannot easily be separated from the flour again afterwards, so the change is an irreversible one.

Plaster of Paris is used to make casts for broken limbs.

Plaster of Paris and water

- When water is mixed with plaster of Paris powder it makes a white liquid.
- The liquid sets to a hard, solid white plaster. This is also irreversible.

If you make a model volcano with a hole in the centre you can fill it with bicarbonate of soda and vinegar - and create a mini eruption!

Baking powder and water

- When baking powder and water are mixed, carbon dioxide gas is made.
- Bubbles form and escape into the air.

Vinegar and bicarbonate of soda

- Mixing vinegar and bicarbonate of soda produces a huge amount of carbon dioxide gas.
- The mixture froths and fizzes before the carbon dioxide escapes into the air.

A Which substance:

1. ... makes bubbles of carbon dioxide gas when mixed with water?

2. ... makes a sticky dough when mixed with water?

3. ... makes a white solid when mixed with water?

Heating and burning

Learning objective: to know that heating and burning can cause irreversible changes

When a substance is heated its temperature rises. If the temperature rises high enough the substance may burst into flame and is said to be burning.

Heating
- Irreversible changes take place when food is cooked.
- Clay is soft and can be shaped. But when it is heated in a kiln the clay becomes hard and rigid. It cannot be softened again.

Burning
- Wood (a solid) burns away to make ash (solid), smoke (tiny solid particles), water vapour (gas) and carbon dioxide (gas).
- As candle wax burns it changes into carbon dioxide (gas) and water vapour (gas).

B

1. What two things do both wood and a candle make as they burn?

2. Which are reversible and which are irreversible changes? Tick the correct columns.

Process	Reversible	Irreversible
Melting of wax		
Burning of wood		
Baking bread		
Freezing water		
Mixing flour and water		

DEFINITION

kiln: An oven or furnace that can generate a very high heat for baking clay into pottery, bricks and tiles.

Look at some meat and vegetables before and after they are cooked. How do they change?

Gravity

Learning objective: to learn about gravity and its relationship with weight

The force of gravity acts between everything in the Universe, and creates a force called weight.

Gravity and the Universe

- The force of gravity acts between every two objects in the Universe.
- Its effects can only be seen and felt if one of the objects is small (like you) and the other is very large (like the Earth).
- Gravity acts between the Sun and the planets and keeps them in orbit.

Gravity on Earth

- The force of gravity acts between everything on the Earth's surface and the centre of the Earth.
- The pull of gravity on your body also makes your body push downwards on things below it. We call this pushing force weight.

Gravity on the Moon

- The Moon is smaller than the Earth. When astronauts visit the Moon, the Moon's pull is smaller than the pull of the Earth's gravity.
- This makes the astronauts weigh six times less than they do on Earth.

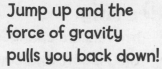

Jump up and the force of gravity pulls you back down!

A

Can you answer these questions about gravity? Write your answers in the spaces below.

1. Can you explain why things fall down holes?

2. If an astronaut weighs 660 newtons on Earth, how much would he weigh on the Moon?

3. A rock on the Moon weighs 10 newtons. How much would it weigh on Earth?

Two forces in action

Learning objective: to know that more than one force can act on an object at once

If you hold this book, gravity pulls it down and the forces in your muscles push it up.

Force meter

- The weight of an object suspended from a force meter makes the spring inside it stretch until its tension force pulls up with the same strength.
- The weight of the object can then be read on the scale on the side of the force meter.

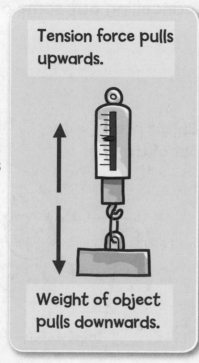

Tension force pulls upwards.

Weight of object pulls downwards.

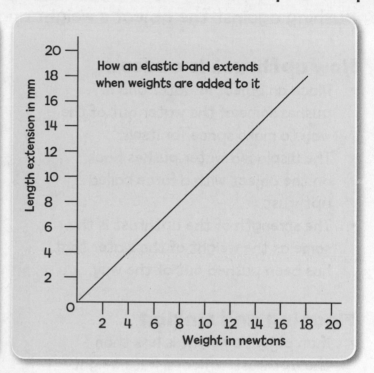

How an elastic band extends when weights are added to it

Length extension in mm

Weight in newtons

Magnetic force

- When a paper clip is put on the end of a magnet it does not fall away.
- This is because the pull of the magnetic force matches the pull of gravity.

B

An elastic band was held up and weights were added to it. After each weight was added the length of the elastic band was measured. The results are plotted on the line graph above.

1. What does the graph show?

2. How much is the elastic band stretched when the weight is 6 newtons?

3. What weight is added to make the elastic band stretch to 12mm?

4. There isn't a reading for when a 20 newton weight was attached. Can you guess why?

Upthrust

Learning objective: to learn that water pushes upwards on objects placed in it

An object placed in water appears to lose weight. A force called upthrust is pushing against the object's weight and cancelling out some of its force.

How upthrust is caused

- Place an object in water and it pushes some of the water out of the way to make space for itself.
- The displaced water pushes back on the object with a force called upthrust.
- The strength of the upthrust is the same as the weight of the water that has been pushed out of the way.

Floating and sinking

- If an object's weight is less than the upthrust, it floats. If its weight is greater than the upthrust, the object sinks.

Object pushes water out of the way

Displaced water pushes back

A

Six objects were put in water. This table shows their weight and upthrust in newtons (N).

Object	Weight (N)	Upthrust (N)
1	50	60
2	45	30
3	6	10
4	25	29
5	73	69
6	105	128

1. Which objects floated?
2. What would happen to object 4 if its weight was increased to 35N?

Air resistance

Learning objective: to know that air resistance pushes on objects that move through it

The strength of the air resistance on an object depends on the size of its surface area pushing through the air.

Gravity and air resistance

- When an object falls gravity pulls it down and air resistance pushes upwards on it.

Testing falling spinners

You can make a spinner by cutting and folding a piece of paper and attaching a paper clip to the lower end to help it fall and spin.

1. Mark these lines on a piece of A4 paper.

2. Cut along the solid lines and fold along the dashed lines.

3. Attach the paperclip weight and test your spinner.

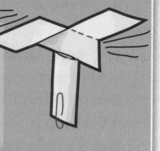

The effect of wing size can be investigated by making spinners with differently sized wings, then letting them fall from the same height and timing how long they take to reach the ground.

B

Three spinners were dropped five times and their falls were timed.

Spinner wing length (cm)	Trial 1 fall (secs)	Trial 2 fall (secs)	Trial 3 fall (secs)	Trial 4 fall (secs)	Trial 5 fall (secs)	Average fall (secs)
3	2	3	4	2	4	
6	4	5	6	5	5	
10	7	8	6	8	6	

1. Fill in the average time for each spinner to fall (add up the fall times of each one and divide by 5).

2. What do the results show?

3. How can the result be explained?

Light rays

Learning objective: to understand that light rays travel from a light source

Light sources send out light rays. When light rays enter our eyes we see.

Light ray

- Light rays travel in straight lines.
- Cut a slit in a piece of card and stick the card on the front of a torch. Shine the torch across a piece of paper. This makes a light ray.
- A light ray is drawn in a diagram as an arrow showing the direction it is travelling.

Light ray and a mirror

- Place a mirror on the paper and shine the torch at it from one side.
- A light ray is seen coming from the mirror.
- This is a reflected light ray.

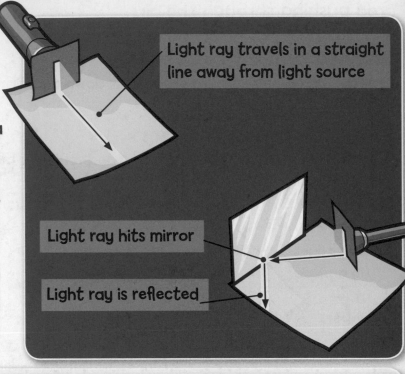

Light ray travels in a straight line away from light source

Light ray hits mirror

Light ray is reflected

A In the space below draw a light ray coming from a torch onto a book and being reflected into an eye. Make sure you add the arrows correctly. Also add labels to explain what's happening.

DEFINITION

light source: Something that gives out light, for example the Sun, the stars, a lamp or a torch.

Reflected light

Learning objective: to know that different surfaces reflect light
in different ways

The angle at which a light ray strikes a mirror affects the angle at which the reflected light ray leaves it.

Comparing angles
- Lines can be drawn on paper to show the path of the striking ray, the reflected ray and the surface of the mirror.
- A line called the normal is drawn at right angles to the mirror where the rays meet.
- A protractor can be used to measure the angles of the rays.

Comparing surfaces
- The material from which a surface is made affects its power to reflect light.
- Shine a torch on to different surfaces.
- Compare the brightness of the reflected light.

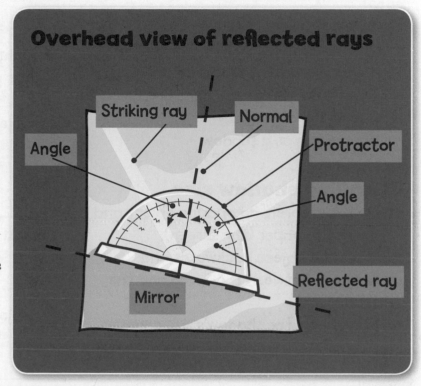

Overhead view of reflected rays

Striking ray · Normal · Angle · Protractor · Angle · Reflected ray · Mirror

B

This table shows the results of two complete measurements and two missing measurements.

1. Can you predict and fill in the missing measurements below?

Angle of striking ray	Angle of reflected ray
20	20
30	
63	63
	77

2. How do the two angles compare? Can you explain why?

Shadows

Learning objective: to learn how shadows form and how their size can change

A shadow forms when light rays are stopped from travelling. Its size depends on the position of the light source and screen.

How shadows are made

- When a light ray strikes an opaque object, its path is blocked.
- There is an absence of light on the other side of the object.
- We see this as a shadow.

Changing shadow size

- Line up a torch, an opaque object and a piece of paper (the screen).
- Move the object backwards and forwards between the torch and the screen.
- Notice how the shadow's size changes.

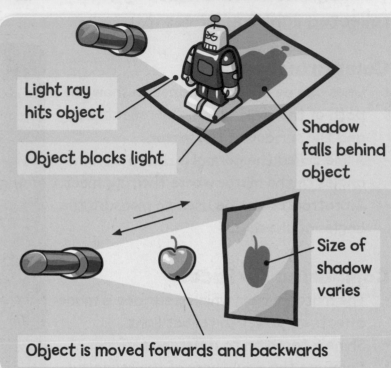

Light ray hits object

Object blocks light

Shadow falls behind object

Size of shadow varies

Object is moved forwards and backwards

A

Experimental set-up	Width of shadow (cm)
Object halfway between torch and screen	10
Torch moved closer to object	15
Torch moved away from object	7
Screen moved closer to object	9
Screen moved away from object	16
Object moved nearer screen	6

1. Predict the size of the shadow when the object is moved away from the screen. Does it become larger or smaller?

2. How can the size of the object's shadow be increased?

DEFINITION

opaque: A material or object that does not allow light to pass through.

screen: A surface onto which light is shone.

Shadows and reflections

Learning objective: to be able to compare shadows and reflections

Shadows and reflections have different appearances.

Shadows

- A shadow has an outline. This is made by rays of light, which pass over the edges of the object and shine onto the surface behind. Inside the outline it is dark.
- No features on the object's surface can be seen in the shadow.

Reflections

- When light rays strike a very smooth surface they all change direction together.
- When the light reaches your eyes you can see a picture in the shiny surface. This is a reflection. Scientists call it an image.
- The image is a picture of where the light rays came from before they hit the surface. The image is reversed.
- All the features on the object's surface can be seen in the image.

B

Read the statements below. Tick the boxes to say whether you think they are true or false.

1. Shadows are made by opaque objects. True ☐ False ☐
2. Reflections are made when light is absent. True ☐ False ☐
3. You can see lots of detail of the object in a shadow. True ☐ False ☐
4. You can see lots of detail of the object in a reflection. True ☐ False ☐
5. Another name for shadow is image. True ☐ False ☐
6. When you wave your left hand in a mirror it looks like your right hand is waving. True ☐ False ☐

7. Write your name on a piece of paper. Easy! Now place a mirror on the paper and look at the paper in the mirror. Try to write your name now. What happens?

Electrical components

An electrical circuit is made up of components. Each one has a symbol.

Battery

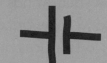

- A battery is also known as a cell. It provides the electricity for the circuit.
- The positive terminal of the battery must be connected to a negative terminal. If they are not connected electricity will not flow in the circuit.

 Wire

- Wires conduct electricity between the different components of a circuit.

Lamp

- The thin wire in the bulb releases light when electricity flows through it.

  **Switch**

open   closed

- When a switch is open electricity cannot flow.
- When it is closed electricity can flow round the circuit.

Motor

- The motor produces a turning movement when electricity flows through it.

 Buzzer

- The buzzer makes a sound when electricity flows through it.
- The red wire must be connected to the positive terminal of a battery for the buzzer to work.

A

Cover the top part of this page. Then, in the spaces below, draw a symbol for:

Motor   Battery   Buzzer   Lamp   Open switch

Circuit diagrams

Scientists use the symbols for electrical components to make circuit diagrams. These are accurate records of circuits, which are quick to make.

A diagram of a circuit with a switch, a battery and a lamp

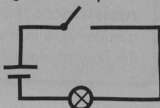

A diagram of a circuit with a switch, two batteries and a motor

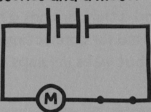

B

1. Have a go at drawing a circuit diagram for a circuit with two batteries, a switch and a buzzer in the space below.

2. Have a go at drawing a circuit diagram for a circuit with a battery, two lamps in a line and a switch in the space below.

Resistance

Learning objective: to know that electrical components resist the flow of electricity

All electrical components, except batteries, have wire in them to allow electricity to flow through them. The wire offers some resistance to the electric current.

Wire thickness and resistance

- A thick wire has a low resistance to an electric current and a thin wire has a high resistance.
- The wires used for connecting components have a low resistance but wires in lamps have a high resistance.

DEFINITION

resistance: The property of a metal wire that slows down the flow of electricity through it.

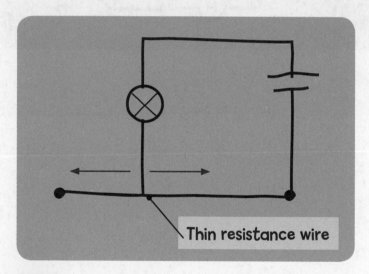

Thin resistance wire

Resistance and length

- A long, thin wire made from a metal with a high resistance is used to investigate how wire length affects resistance.
- The picture shows the loose end of a wire connecting a short length of resistance wire into the circuit.
- The arrow shows how the loose end can be moved along the resistance wire to increase its length in the circuit.
- The lamp shines brightly when the resistance is low and dimly when the resistance is high.

A

Look at the circuit diagram above and answer these questions.

1. Will the lamp shine brightly or dimly when a short length of resistance wire is used?

2. Will the lamp shine brightly or dimly when a long length of resistance wire is used?

3. How will the brightness of the bulb change when the loose end is moved to the right?

Batteries and lamps

Learning objective: to know that the brightness of lamps can
be changed

Batteries supply electricity to circuits. Lamps offer resistance to current flow.

The flow of electricity in a circuit is affected by changing the number of batteries or lamps in it.

Batteries and power
- A battery's power to generate electricity is measured in volts (V).
- When batteries are added to a circuit their voltage combines to give greater power.

Lamps and resistance
- The high resistance wire inside each lamp lights up when the current flows.
- If two lamps are joined in a row, or 'in series', the resistance to the current doubles. Both lamps shine less brightly.
- If two lamps are joined side by side, or 'in parallel', the resistance of one does not add to the resistance of the other. Both lamps shine as brightly as though they were alone in the circuit.

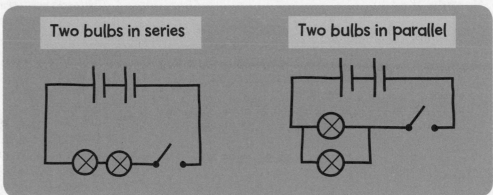

Two bulbs in series   Two bulbs in parallel

B Have a go at answering these questions about resistance, batteries and lamps.

1. What is the voltage when three 1.5V batteries are put in a circuit?

2. What is the voltage in the circuit when two of the three batteries are taken out?

3. Two lamps are arranged in series in a circuit with one battery. Then a third lamp is added to the series. Do the lamps shine more brightly or more dimly?

Answers

Pages 10–11

A
1. 0.2
2. 0.35
3. 0.71
4. 0.96
5. 8.18
6. 8.4
7. 8.53
8. 8.79
9. 8.95
10. 16.18
11. 16.4
12. 16.53
13. 16.79
14. 16.99

B
Leatherback turtle	462.9kg
Green sea turtle	355.3kg
Loggerhead turtle	257.8kg
Flatback turtle	78.15kg
Hawksbill turtle	62.65kg
Kemp's Ridley turtle	60.45kg

C
2. 3.58, 3.85, 5.38, 5.83, 8.35, 8.53

Pages 12–13

A
1. 13.5
2. 96.7
3. 6.85
4. 33.46

B
1. 35 litres
2. 98.5km
3. 25kg

C

×10

8.2	82	820
0.82	8.2	82
0.082	0.82	8.2

÷10

×10

0.6	6	60
0.06	0.6	6
0.006	0.06	0.6

÷10

Pages 14–15

A
1. 6
2. 16
3. 7
4. 18
5. 9
6. 12
7. 5
8. 6
9. 7
10. 63
11. 9
12. 6

B
1. 20
2. 5
3. 16
4. 11
5. 12
6. 5
7. 2
8. 47

C
1. 19 − (12 − 5) = 12
2. 16 − (10 − 6) = 12
3. 22 − (5 + 5) = 12
4. (6 + 13) − 7 = 12
   or 6 + (13 − 7) = 12
5. (24 − 6) − 6 = 12
6. 20 − (10 − 2) = 12

D
1. 48
2. 7
3. 8
4. 21
5. 9
6. 20

Pages 16–17

A and B

×	0	1	2	3	4	5	6	7	8	9	10
0	0	0	0	0	0	0	0	0	0	0	0
1	0	1	2	3	4	5	6	7	8	9	10
2	0	2	4	6	8	10	12	14	16	18	20
3	0	3	6	9	12	15	18	21	24	27	30
4	0	4	8	12	16	20	24	28	32	36	40
5	0	5	10	15	20	25	30	35	40	45	50
6	0	6	12	18	24	30	36	42	48	54	60
7	0	7	14	21	28	35	42	49	56	63	70
8	0	8	16	24	32	40	48	56	64	72	80
9	0	9	18	27	36	45	54	63	72	81	90
10	0	10	20	30	40	50	60	70	80	90	100

C
1. 24, 48
2. 15, 12
3. 46
4. 18, 77
5. 6, 50
6. 39, 92

D
1. 16
2. 49
3. 36
4. 81
5. 1
6. 4
7. 100
8. 9
9. 64
10. 25

Pages 18–19

A
1. (1, 8) (2, 4)
2. (1, 20) (2, 10) (4, 5)
3. (1, 24) (2, 12) (3, 8) (4, 6)
4. (1, 28) (2, 14) (4, 7)

B
1. 4, 8, 12, 16, 20, 24, 28, 32, 36, 40
2. 3, 6, 9, 12, 15, 18, 21, 24, 27, 30
3. 6, 12, 18, 24, 30, 36, 42, 48, 54, 60
4. 5, 10, 15, 20, 25, 30, 35, 40, 45, 50
5. 10, 20, 30, 40, 50, 60, 70, 80, 90, 100
6. 8, 16, 24, 32, 40, 48, 56, 64, 72, 80

C
1. 15, 30
2. 12, 24
3. 20, 40
4. 24, 48
5. 30, 60
6. 12, 24, 36

D

Factor of 24 | Multiple of 3

10, 2, 4, 1, 16 | 12, 3, 24, 6 | 15, 20, 9, 30, 18, 25

Pages 20–21

A
1. The number 5 cannot be divided by 2 or 3 or 4.
   So the number 5 is prime.
2. The number 6 can be divided by 2 or 3. So the number 6 is not prime.
3. The number 7 cannot be divided by 2 or 3 or 4 or 5 or 6. So the number 7 is prime.
4. The number 3 cannot be divided by 2. So the number 3 is prime.
5. The number 8 can be divided by 2 or 4. So the number 8 is not prime.
6. The number 11 cannot be divided by 2 or 3 or 4 or 5 or 6 or 7 or 8 or 9 or 10. So the number 11 is prime.

B The hidden primes are: 7, 11, 13, 17, 19, 23, 29

C They can't be divided whatever you do.
The smallest prime is number two.
Then come three and five and seven.
The next prime is of course eleven.
Thirteen is next upon the scene.
Seventeen follows, and then nineteen.

Pages 22–23

A
1. 9468
2. 7803
3. 4479

B
1. 9625
2. 9803
3. 6078
4. 7869
5. 7077
6. 6435

C
1. 3420km
2. 5803km
3. 6281km
4. 4849km
5. 4490km

D

```
    4  6 [3] 8
+   9 [1] 6 [3]
 [1] 3  8  0 [1]
```

Pages 24–25

A
1. 3146
2. 5668
3. 4370

B
1. 3847 − 1762 = 2085
2. 7943 − 2486 = 5457
3. 4115 − 2936 = 1179

172

C 1. 1161m

2. 1381m

3. 1279m

4. Caribbean and Bering

5. Caribbean

6. Indian and Atlantic

Pages 26-27

A 1. 1444   2. 3108

3. 456   4. 3286

B 1. 720 hours   3. 700g

2. 928km   4. 735

C

Items	Amount in 1 pack	Number of packs	Total number of items
Pencils	28	76	2128
Chalk	15	33	495
Sharpeners	26	19	494
Erasers	48	14	672
Pens	52	58	3016
Crayons	34	47	1608

D 1. 543 x 6 = 3258

2. 456 x 3 = 1368

3. 456 x 3 = 1368

Pages 28-29

A 1. 162 r2   3. 47 r1

2. 73 r2   4. 231 r2

B 1 ⟶ 271 ÷ 6

2 ⟶ 608 ÷ 3

3 ⟶ 315 ÷ 8

4 ⟶ 454 ÷ 5

5 ⟶ 149 ÷ 6

6 ⟶ 398 ÷ 7

7 ⟶ 259 ÷ 9

8 ⟶ 458 ÷ 9

9 ⟶ 359 ÷ 10

C

Day of the week	Eggs collected	Number of Full boxes (6 eggs)	Eggs left over
Monday	627	104	3
Tuesday	572	95	2
Wednesday	700	116	4
Thursday	644	107	2
Friday	683	113	5
Saturday	594	99	0
Sunday	735	122	3

Pages 30-31

A Liverpool - 469000

Bradford - 293700

Sheffield - 439900

Derby - 229400

Birmingham - 970900

Nottingham - 249600

Bristol - 420600

Plymouth - 243800

B 1. 800   4. 1200

2. 500   5. 5900

3. 100   6. 13700

C 1. 16kg   2. 21kg

3. 34kg   4. 45kg

D 1. 0.93   2. 7.08

3. 12.95   4. 7.59

5. 2.91   6. 30.08

Pages 32-33

A 1. 67.83   3. 91.81

2. 84.76   4. 85.51

B 1. 43.02   3. 37.76

2. 47.23   4. 41.78

C 1. 26.63 l   3. 68.01kg

2. 63.91m   4. 81.23m

D 1. 0.76   4. 0.09

2. 0.51   5. 1.34

3. Eileen and Nikki

Pages 34-35

A 1. 6 ÷ 3 = 2   21 ÷ 3 = 7

So 6/21 is the same as 2/7.

2. 9 ÷ 3 = 3   15 ÷ 3 = 5

So 9/15 is the same as 3/5.

3. 4 ÷ 2 = 2   6 ÷ 2 = 3

So 4/6 is the same as 2/3.

4. 12 ÷ 6 = 2   18 ÷ 6 = 3

So 12/18 is the same as 2/3.

B 1. 15 ÷ 5 = 3   40 ÷ 5 = 8

So 15/40 is the same as 3/8

2. 14 ÷ 2 = 7   16 ÷ 2 = 8

So 14/16 is the same as 7/8

3. 8 ÷ 2 = 4   12 ÷ 2 = 6

So 8/12 is the same as 4/6

4. 20 ÷ 10 = 2   30 ÷ 10 = 3

So 20/30 is the same as 2/3

Other possible answers:

20 ÷ 5 = 4   30 ÷ 5 = 6

So 20/30 is the same as 4/6

20 ÷ 2 = 10   30 ÷ 2 = 15

So 20/30 is the same as 10/15

C 9/18 and 1/2.

10/15 and 2/3.

18/24 and 3/4.

7/28 and 1/4.

12/15 and 4/5.

50/60 and 5/6.

11/33 and 1/3

Pages 36-37

A

1. $\frac{1}{3} = \frac{2}{6} = \frac{3}{9} = \frac{4}{12} = \frac{5}{15} = \frac{6}{18}$

2. $\frac{1}{4} = \frac{2}{8} = \frac{3}{12} = \frac{4}{16} = \frac{5}{20} = \frac{6}{24}$

3. $\frac{1}{2} = \frac{2}{4} = \frac{3}{6} = \frac{4}{8} = \frac{5}{10} = \frac{6}{12}$

4. $\frac{2}{3} = \frac{4}{6} = \frac{6}{9} = \frac{8}{12} = \frac{10}{15} = \frac{12}{18}$

B 1. >

2. <

3. <

4. >

C

0	0.1	0.2	0.3	0.4		0.6	0.7	0.8	0.9	1
		0.25			0.5		0.75			

0.1 ⟶ $\frac{1}{10}$ 0.2 ⟶ $\frac{1}{5}$

0.25 ⟶ $\frac{1}{4}$ 0.3 ⟶ $\frac{3}{10}$

0.4 ⟶ $\frac{2}{5}$ 0.5 ⟶ $\frac{1}{2}$

0.6 ⟶ $\frac{6}{10}$ and 0.6 ⟶ $\frac{3}{5}$

0.7 ⟶ $\frac{7}{10}$ 0.75 ⟶ $\frac{3}{4}$

0.8 ⟶ $\frac{4}{5}$ 0.9 ⟶ $\frac{9}{10}$

Answers

Page 37 cont.

D 1. $\frac{1}{4}$, $\frac{3}{8}$, $\frac{1}{2}$, $\frac{10}{16}$

2. $\frac{1}{6}$, $\frac{1}{3}$, $\frac{6}{12}$, $\frac{3}{4}$

Pages 38-39

A 1. 30% 5. 80%
2. 20% 6. 10%
3. 7% 7. 65%
4. 22% 8. 12%

B 1. 0.5 4. 2/5
2. 25% 5. 0.34
3. 5% 6. 70%

C 1. 1/4, 25% 4. 3/10, 30%
2. 4/8, 50% 5. 2/5, 40%
3. 7/10, 70% 6. 4/8, 50%

D 1. 1% 3. 80%
2. 80% 4. 80%

Pages 40-41

A 1. $\frac{2}{5}$ 2. $\frac{4}{5}$ 3. $\frac{1}{4}$

B 1. 70% 4. 84%
2. 90% 5. 76%
3. 80%

C 1. 7cm 5. 35ml
2. 27km 6. 20m
3. 4 litres 7. 60g
4. 12kg 8. 200mm

D

	50%	25%	10%	40%	5%
60m	30m	15m	6m	24m	3m
50m	25m	12.5m	5m	20m	2.5m
300m	150m	75m	30m	120m	15m
250m	125m	62.5m	25m	100m	12.5m

Pages 42-43

A

1. $\frac{1}{3}$ 2. $\frac{1}{4}$

3. $\frac{1}{2}$ 4. $\frac{2}{3}$

5. $\frac{2}{5}$ 6. $\frac{3}{4}$

B

1.

Pineapples	Oranges	Total
1	4	5
2	8	10
5	20	25
8	32	40
10	40	50

2.

Bananas	Peaches	Total
2	3	5
4	6	10
12	18	30
16	24	40
20	30	50

C 1. butter 150g   flour 200g
carrots 100g   sugar 60g
eggs 50g   walnuts 40g
2. flour 180g   butter 90g
sugar 60g   choc chips 30g

D butter 300g   flour 400g
carrots 200g   sugar 120g
eggs 100g   walnuts 80g

Pages 44-45

A 1. triangle 4. hexagon
2. quadrilateral 5. heptagon
3. pentagon 6. octagon

B 1. rectangle 2. parallelogram
3. trapezium 4. square
5. kite 6. rhombus

C 1. always 4. always
2. never 5. sometimes
3. always 6. always

Pages 46-47

A

Straight angle	4.
Acute	1.
Obtuse	2.
Right angle	3.

B

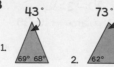

C

D

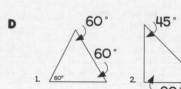

Pages 48-49

A 1. rotated 2. reflected
3. translated 4. reflected
5. translated 6. rotated

Pages 50-51

A 1. (3, 5) 2. (8, 8)

B 1. Triangle B
(4, 1) (6, 4) (7, 1)
2. Triangle C
(0, 3) (3, 2) (3, 6)
Triangle D
(5, 2) (5, 6) (8, 3)
3. Triangle E
(0, 5) (4, 5) (4, 8)
Triangle F
(4, 2) (4, 5) (8, 5)

Pages 52-53

A 1. A triangular prism has 2 triangular faces and 3 rectangular faces.
2. A cube has 6 square faces.
3. A tetrahedron has 4 triangular faces.
4. A hexagonal prism has 2 hexagonal faces and 6 rectangular faces.
5. A square-based pyramid has 1 square face and 4 triangular faces.

6. A cuboid has 4 rectangular faces and 2 square faces.

B

	A	B	C	D	E	F	G	H
Prism	✔	✔	✔	✔	✔			✔
Pyramid						✔	✔	

Pages 54–55

A 1. 5.8cm   2. 1067cm
    3. 9.1m   4. 135mm
    5. 8300m   6. 9.4cm
    7. 3.7km   8. 146mm
B 1. 35mm   2. 52mm
    3. 26mm   4. 18mm
    5. 63mm   6. 37mm
C 1. 108mm   2. 112mm
    3. 175mm   4. 96mm

Pages 56–57

A 1. $28cm^2$ 3. $42cm^2$
    2. $45cm^2$ 4. $80cm^2$
B 1. $18cm^2$ 3. $16cm^2$
    2. $10cm^2$ 4. $15cm^2$
C 1. $24cm^2$ 4. $33cm^2$
    2. $19cm^2$ 5. $30cm^2$
    3. $54cm^2$ 6. $48cm^2$

Pages 58–59

A 1. 10:25   2. 09:55
    3. 19:00   4. 16:30
    5. 09:47   6. 17:25
B 1. 1.50pm   2. 11.08am
    3. 9.22am   4. 11.10pm
    5. 3.59pm   6. 9.34pm
C Alarm wake up
    7.00am   07:00
    Meet for coffee
    10.00am   10:00
    Dentist
    11.35am   11:35
    Bus time
    2.18pm   14:18
    Taxi
    7.15pm   19:15

Amazing Maths
7.40pm   19:40
D 20:10   20.10.2010

Pages 60–61

A 1. 4/mode
    2. 4/median
B 1. 140cm   4. 1
    2. 140cm   5. Amy
    3. 150cm   6. 145cm
C 1. Median 10cm
    2. Mode 10cm
    3. Mean 10cm
    Challenge
    4. Median 2 hours
    5. Mode 2 hours
    6. Mean 3 hours

Pages 62 – 63

A 1. There is an evens chance of picking a multiple of 2.
    2. There is a certain chance of picking a diamond.
    3. There is a poor chance of picking a multiple of 5.
    4. There is a poor chance of picking a number over 6.
    5. It is impossible to pick the queen of diamonds.
    6. There is a poor chance of picking the 9 of diamonds.
B 1. 1 in 6   2. 1 in 2
    3. 1 in 3   4. 1 in 3
    5. 1 in 2   6. 1 in 6
C 1. 12 red   2. 6 green
    3. 4 blue   4. 2 black
    5. 0 yellow

Answers

Page 65

A television: vision, is, on
cupboard: cup, board, boar, oar
wardrobe: ward, robe, rob, war
supermarket: super, market, mark
subway: sub, way
basketball: basket, ball, ask, all
crossword: cross, word, or

B On Saturday, we took the train into town. We usually go by car because Mum says the train fare is too dear, but she agrees it's much faster by train. We even had a drink on the train, which we can't do in the car! We didn't need to pay for parking either so I think the train was cheaper in the end!

Page 66

A 1. bananas
girls
boys
days
stars
2. potatoes
buses
boxes
dishes
watches
dresses
tomatoes
brushes
benches
glasses
wishes
volcanoes

Page 67

B 1. leaves
knives
calves
2. babies
butterflies
ponies
stories
parties
ladies
3. geese
sheep
deer
feet
children
women

Page 68

A 1. autograph
telescope
automatic
automobile
telephone
autobiography
2. anti-ageing = not ageing or stops ageing
anti-bacterial = not bacterial or stops bacteria
anti-freeze = stops freezing

B Toothpaste has an anti-bacterial ingredient.

Page 69

C magician: someone who performs magic tricks
pianist: someone who plays the piano
chemist: someone who works with chemicals
beautician: someone who works in beauty
electrician: someone who works with electricity
musician: someone who plays a musical instrument
politician: someone who works in politics
biologist: someone who works in biology

D singer, gardener, teacher, climber, walker, player

Page 70

A When Superboy whispered a secret word, his school jumper became a long, shiny, red cloak and his spectacles morphed into a mirrored, black mask. His super-human powers enabled him to climb vertical walls, scale rooftops, sense danger and bring wrong-doers to justice.

B All of a sudden, the rock door split open and a dark figure sprang out! It was the Evil Weevil, Superboy's deadliest enemy. Weevil eyed him menacingly for a second and lunged forward with a blood-curdling battle cry!

Page 71

C How was Superboy going to defeat the Evil Weevil? Was he cunning and clever enough to outwit him? Everyone knew that the Weevil was a wimp really but he was a scary wimp, all the same. What would happen if Superboy failed? Would the Earth be plunged into another inter-planetary war?

D   "So, Superboy, we meet at last," the Weevil sneered. "It's a shame we don't have time to strike up a friendship! Ha, ha, ha!" The Weevil laughed at his own feeble joke.
      "I wouldn't worry, Weevil," replied Superboy. "You'll have plenty of time to make friends with the cockroaches you'll

meet in the state planetary prison!"

Page 72

A 1. I can't find it. It's gone!
2. That's my friend's house.
3. It's Toni's book.
4. Where's Mrs Dale's class?
5. They'll be late for school.
6. We're going to Gina's party.

B can't: cannot, it's: it is, that's: that is, they'll: they will, where's: where is, we're: we are

Page 73

C 1. The clown's car fell apart.
2. The clowns' car fell apart.
3. The dog's owner went to the Pooch Parlour.
4. The dogs' owner went to the Pooch Parlour.
5. The girl's rabbit ran away.
6. The girls' rabbit ran away.
7. The man's sunglasses were expensive.
8. The men's sunglasses were expensive.

Page 74

A 1. It was lucky for me that it was not going to be a problem.
2. The sun was burning hot so we had to put on lashings of sunscreen.
3. She clicked her fingers and the little dog began to dance.

Page 75

B First, we went to the Tower of London to see the Crown Jewels. Next, we saw Big Ben and, after lunch, we had a great time at the London Dungeon. Although it rained for most of the day we didn't really notice, except when we finally got back to the bus station and had to wait ages for the bus to come... in the rain!

C First, we went on the Ghost Train. It wasn't as scary as we thought it was going to be. But then we went on the Rocky Coaster and that was terrifying! We thought we were going to go flying off the track! Next, we got a real soaking on the Log Flume and the Crazy Rapids. Lastly, we had a ride on the Angry Camel and it was so funny that we couldn't stop laughing.

Page 76

A 1. Mr Parker gave Class 5 a detention so they missed their playtime.
2. Our class won the merit prize so we are going on a trip to the zoo.

3. Chris is team captain because he is the best at football.
4. Katie loves swimming so she joined the swimming club.
5. I usually like history but today it was boring.
6. We watched a film about spiders because we were doing a topic on them.

Page 77

B 1. It's mine.
2. This is yours.
3. The coats are theirs.
4. The cat is hers.
5. The dog eats its dinner.

Page 78

A I drew, I wrote, I swam, I caught, I saw, I went

Page 79

C You could have: 1. The giant stomped angrily across the room.
2. "Hubble, bubble, toil and trouble," cackled the witch menacingly.
3. The elf sneaked quietly into the shop.
4. The vampire suddenly leaped out of the coffin.
5. The wizard carefully concocted a potion.
6. The boy quickly snatched the wand.

Page 81

B 1. Joe's a sly fox! Joe might have done something behind someone's back.
2. Jen's a rock. Jen is loyal and someone you can depend on.

D 1. As hard as nails
2. As strong as an ox
3. As weak as a kitten
4. As white as a sheet
5. As cold as ice
6. As red as a beetroot

Page 82

A 1. Things become easier with practice.
2. Fix something now before it gets worse.
3. Think before you act.
4. Don't question generosity.
5. Don't ask too many people to do one job.

B 1. I'm not feeling very well.
2. He looked foolish because he was wrong.
3. It's raining heavily.
4. Things are going well.

Answers

Page 83

C 1. The balloon burst with a loud pop.
2. The glass smashed onto the floor.
3. My feet squelched in thick mud.
4. The heavy door closed with a thud.
5. The bees buzzed around the flowers.
6. The waves crashed onto the rocks.
7. The drink fizzed in the can.

D 1. A gaggle of geese
2. A pack of wolves
3. A pride of lions
4. A herd of cows
5. A flock of birds
6. A swarm of bees
7. A school of dolphins

Page 85

A 1. 2nd, 2. 3rd, 3. 1st

B I felt betrayed. Lisa was my best friend.
We'd been friends since we were four years old and at nursery together. But now I'd seen a note written on a page in Lisa's Pony Diary: 'Number one best friend: Becky. Number two best friend: Emily.'

Page 87

A 1. He/she was less afraid of the captain than everyone else.
2. He was a scary and angry man who, when he drank too much, would often fly into a rage.
3. He would "sit and sing his wicked, old, wild sea-songs" and tell stories.
4. They were afraid that if they didn't sing loudly the captain would notice them and might kill them.
5. He would get angry when they asked questions or, sometimes, when they didn't ask questions, because he thought they weren't listening.
6. He slapped his hand on the table when he wanted silence.
7. The person telling the story is someone who knew the captain well and had seen him at the inn many times.

Page 89

A 1. goeth, seizeth, doth, 'tis.
2. The poet's name is John Bunyan.
3. He died in 1688.
4. Any of these pairs rhyme: sure/endure; on/upon; go/so; sure/procure.
5. The snail eats flowers or leaves.
6. Other animals travel a long way and look for food but do not find it.
7. The snail goes slowly but she gets there in the end. If we follow her steady example, we can get what we want too.

Page 90

A The missing letter in each word is 's'.

Page 91

B Rhymes: hands/lands/stands; crawls/walls/falls
Alliterations: clasps/crag/crooked/close; lonely/lands; watches/walls

Page 93

A "Greetings, Sir, on this the three hundred and sixty-sixth day of term!" exclaimed Bot brightly, as he entered the date on the touch-screen learning wall.
   "Give out the books please, Bot," said 1471.
   "Do you mean those curious, pre-computer-age page-turners, Sir? We haven't used those for over a thousand years!" said Bot.
   "I know we haven't, but I thought we'd start with an ancient history lesson today!" replied 1471.

Page 95

A 1. They were at war because the Greek queen, Helen, had been kidnapped by Paris, the Trojan prince.
2. Odysseus was a Greek.
3. They believed the war was over because they saw the Greek ships sailing away.
4. He was very important because he persuaded the Trojans that the horse was lucky.
5. They were happy that the war was over.
6. Yes, Odysseus' trick worked because the Greeks rescued Helen and destroyed Troy.

Page 97

A 1. One of the biggest species of jellyfish is found in the Antarctic Sea.
2. One of the deadliest jellyfish is the Box Jelly.
3. Jellyfish eat shrimps, plankton and microscopic fish, or even other jellyfish.
4. Jellyfish are prey to creatures that don't fear their tentacles, e.g. turtles or other jellyfish.

Page 100

A These words were misspelt: was, father, able, married, writer.

Page 101

B 1. He was 58 years old when he died.
2. Dates are important in a biography because they help us to structure our writing and to better understand events in people's lives.
3. 1812: Charles Dickens was born in 1812.
   1824: His father was sent to prison in 1824.
   1829: He began his career as a journalist in 1829.
   1836: He got married in 1836 and he published his first book.
   1870: He died in 1870.

Page 103

A 1. Inedible means not good enough to eat.
2. Although we had a wonderful view of the rubbish bins.
3. Firstly, secondly, thirdly, finally.
4. A 'cupboard' is a metaphor for the room they stayed in.
5. It would have been difficult for him to stop the cicadas!
6. The address states Naples, Italy.

Page 106

A 1. Several answers are possible:
Big and black, a crow screeched in the darkness.
In the darkness, a crow, big and black, screeched.
A big and black crow screeched in the darkness.
In the darkness, a big and black crow screeched.
2. Startled, Jack held his breath.
Jack held his breath, startled.
3. With horror, he realized a creature was creeping towards him.
A creature was creeping towards him, he realized with horror.
4. Like some kind of terrible warning, a church bell rang close by.
Close by, a church bell rang, like some kind of terrible warning.
Close by, like some kind of terrible warning, a church bell rang.

B Jack started to run. He ran down the hill and along the hedge, looking for the gate. It was there somewhere, but in the dark, he just couldn't find it. He knew he didn't have much time.
"I wonder where Jack is," said his mother, looking anxiously at the kitchen clock. "He's going to be late for his tea!"
The thing on the hill lifted its head to gaze at the moon. It snuffled the cold, clear air. Then it let out a long, blood-curdling howl and lumbered after Jack.

C The two wrongly placed sentences are: 'Long, sticky drool slobbered from its jaws.' and 'He glanced anxiously over his shoulder.'

Page 108

A 1. Fairytale castle or forest – Fairy stories
2. School or home – Modern stories
3. Old house or graveyard at night – Spooky stories
4. Remote or faraway place – Adventure stories
5. Other planets – Science fiction stories

B When: in summer. Where: on the beach.
The summer sun is high in the sky. The crashing waves break against my chest as I race towards them with my board. In front of me, I hear my friends shouting and I taste excitement in the salty air.

Page 111

B Possible answers:
My cheeks feel their icy breath.
Now arrows are falling like rain
Towards the enemy they fly.
In his direction the arrows flew
One has hit him in the eye
As I watch Harold die
It's a tragedy, but the war is won!

Page 116

A Adjectives might include: healthy, home-made, tasty, local, best.

Answers

Page 120

A The heart pumps the blood into the arteries and it travels to all parts of the body. The blood returns to the heart in blood vessels called veins.

Page 121

B 65 person lying down, 70 person standing, 90 person walking, 120 person running.

Page 122

A People who are ill take medicines to get better. The medicines can contain drugs to help them recover. Harmful drugs like cocaine make people become addicts. Addicts are in danger of being killed by the drugs they take.

Page 124

A

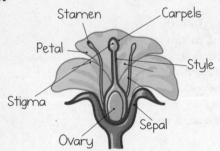

Stamen
Carpels
Petal
Style
Stigma
Sepal
Ovary

Page 125

B

	Insect-pollinated flower	Wind-pollinated flower
Large petals	✓	
Strong scent	✓	
Nectar	✓	
Little pollen	✓	
Lots of pollen		✓
Smooth pollen		✓
Spiky pollen	✓	

Page 126

A Stigma makes pollen grains stick.

Pollen grain carries a substance from a flower for fertilization.

Pollen tube carries a substance from a pollen grain to an ovule.

Page 127

B 1-Seed germinates. 2-Seedling starts to grow.
3-Plant fully grown. 4-Plant makes flowers.
5-Flowers make fruits. 6-Plant disperses fruit.

Page 129

B A frog's egg is surrounded by jelly.
A tadpole hatches from the egg. It has a long tail and looks like a little fish. In time the tadpole grows legs and a big head and its tail disappears. When this happens it has turned into a frog.

Page 130

A 40cm^3

Page 131

B Helium - lighter than air.
Natural gas - used in some cookers.
Carbon dioxide - used to make food by plants.

Page 132

A A piece of chocolate was left on a sunny windowsill. As it got warmer its firm sides started to sag and it began to lose its shape. When the temperature reached melting point the chocolate turned into a liquid and dripped off the windowsill.

Page 133

B

Substance	Freezing point (°C)	
Beeswax	64°C	2
Water	0°C	5
Chocolate	25°C	4
Lard	43°C	3
Pewter	240°C	1

3 would freeze.

Page 134

A Hot, dry, windy air.

Page 135

B

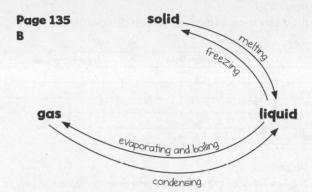

solid

melting

freezing

gas

liquid

evaporating and boiling

condensing

Page 136

A Earth 12,756km.
Moon 3476km.
Sun 1,392,000km.
The Moon is nearer the Earth than the Sun.

Page 138

A 1. Anticlockwise, 2. C, 3. A, 4. B.

Page 139

B 1. False, 2. True, 3. False, 4. True, 5. False,
6. True.

Page 140

A 1. Waxing 1, 2 and 3.
2. Waning 5, 6 and 7.

Page 141

B Neptune, Uranus, Saturn, Jupiter, asteroid belt, Mars,
Earth, Venus, Mercury, Mercury, Venus, Earth, Mars,
asteroid belt, Jupiter, Saturn, Uranus, Neptune.

Page 142

A Sound travels fastest through solids. Sound travels slowest
through gases.

Page 143

B 1. By wrapping the same thickness of each material tested
around the sound source.
2. B was the best insulator.

Page 144

A 2. Bottom C note on piano.
3. Thunder.
4. Ordinary voice.
5. Baby's first cry.
6. Chainsaw.
7. Top note on piano.

Page 145

B 1. Drum B has the lower pitch.
2. String B has the higher pitch.
3. It makes the pitch lower.

Page 146

A 1. When light shines on a leaf it provides energy for water
and carbon dioxide to be changed into food and oxygen.
2. The oxygen made by plants goes into the air where it is
breathed in by animals. These animals then breathe out the
carbon dioxide that plants use to make food.

Page 147

B 1. A tap root is thicker with fewer side roots, which spread
out in the soil. It goes deeper
into the soil.
2. Gravelly soil drains best. (A)
Clay soil has the worst drainage. (C)

Page 148

A 1. Beetle and deer are using the plants
for shelter.
2. A deer is using a plant as food.
3. A spider is using the plant to set a trap.

Page 149

B The animals are A millipede, B earthworm,
C insect, D snail, E harvestman, F slug,
G woodlouse, H spider, I centipede.

Answers

Page 150

A stiff tail feathers, chisel-shaped beak, two toes pointing backwards instead of one, strong claws, strong skull, long tongue.

Page 151

B
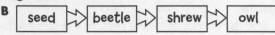

Page 152

A 1. A virus might give you a cold.

2. Bacteria are removed when you clean your teeth.

3. Bacteria and fungi might grow on an orange.

4. Bacteria and fungi make the contents of a compost bin rot.

Page 153

B The bread would not have bubbles in it and its texture would be firm, not spongy. This is because the yeast needs sugar to feed on to make the bread rise.

Page 154

A 1. Sand, flour and custard powder can be separated from the water by filtering.

2. A filter has holes in it that are large enough to let a liquid through, but are too small to let particles of undissolved solids through.

Page 155

B When salt is mixed with water it dissolves and makes a solution. If the solution is boiled the water turns to steam and leaves the salt behind. The steam can be turned to water again by cooling it down in a process called condensing.

Page 156

A All of the statements are correct.

Page 157

B 1. 40 seconds.

2. 40 seconds.

3. 20 degrees Celsius.

Page 158

A 1. baking powder.

2. flour.

3. plaster of Paris.

Page 159

B 1. water vapour (gas) and carbon dioxide (gas).

2.

Process	Reversible	Irreversible
Melting of wax	✓	
Burning of wood		✓
Baking bread		✓
Freezing water	✓	
Mixing flour and water		✓

Page 160

A 1. The force of gravity pulls them down towards the centre of the Earth.

2. 110 newtons.

3. 60 newtons.

Page 161

B 1. How the length of the elastic band extends as weights are attached to it.

2. 6mm.

3. 12 newtons.

4. The elastic band broke.

Page 162

A 1. 1, 3, 4 and 6 floated.

2. It would sink.

Page 163

B 1.

Spinner wing length (cm)	Trial 1 fall (secs)	Trial 2 fall (secs)	Trial 3 fall (secs)	Trial 4 fall (secs)	Trial 5 fall (secs)	Average fall (secs)
3	2	3	4	2	4	3
6	4	5	6	5	5	5
10	7	8	6	8	6	7

2. The larger the wing the slower the fall.

3. The larger wings have a larger air resistance, which slows down the fall.

Page 164

A An arrow should go from the torch to the book. A second arrow should go from the book to the eye.

Page 165

B 1.

Angle of striking ray	Angle of reflected ray
20	20
30	**30**
63	63
77	77

2. The angles are always the same. The light leaves the mirror at the same angle at which it struck it.

Page 166

A 1. It becomes larger.

2. Moving the torch nearer object, screen moved away from object, object moved away from screen.

Page 167

B 1. True.

2. False.

3. False.

4. True.

5. False.

6. True.

Page 168

A

Motor Battery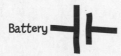

Buzzer Lamp

Open switch

Page 169

B 1. 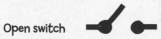   2.

Page 170

A 1. Brightly.

2. Dimly.

3. From dim to bright.

Page 171

B 1. 4.5 V.

2. 1.5 V.

3. More dimly.

Notes

Notes

Notes

Index

Index